CW00821056

Quick Bible Crosswords

Derek Banes

The wider view on the Church

Every week *The Church of England Newspaper* brings you the news from the Church of England, and Anglican churches around the world. With a lively mix of news, features and incisive comment, it is an indispensible way to keep in touch with developments that affect you. From what the bishops are saying in the Houses of Parliament, to developments in your local diocese, and from reviews of the latest movies to the must-read Christian books, and from devotional articles to our recipe of the week, our packed newspaper is a perfect mix every week for the interested Christian.

Try it for yourself. *To request a free sample copy, please write to:*

Circulation Offer,
The Church of England Newspaper,
14 Great College Street,
London, SW1P 3RX
or email:
subs@churchnewspaper.com

www.churchnewspaper.com

Quick
Bible
Crosswords

Text copyright © Derek Banes 2009
The author asserts the moral right
to be identified as the author of this work

Published by
The Bible Reading Fellowship
15 The Chambers, Vineyard
Abingdon OX14 3FE
United Kingdom
Tel: +44 (0)1865 319700
Email: enquiries@brf.org.uk
Website: www.brf.org.uk

ISBN 978 1 84101 712 9

First published 2009
10 9 8 7 6 5 4 3 2 1 0
All rights reserved

Acknowledgments
Extracts from the Authorised Version of the Bible (The King James Bible), the rights in which
are vested in the Crown, are reproduced by permission of the Crown's Patentee, Cambridge
University Press.

A catalogue record for this book is available from the British Library

Printed in Singapore by Craft Print International Ltd

Preface

In 1998 I retired from full-time employment after 34 years as a mechanical engineer. Looking for a way to supplement my company pension, I decided to turn a hobby into an income and try my hand at compiling crosswords rather than solving them. As a result I was asked to produce a weekly crossword on a biblical theme for *The Church of England Newspaper*, for whom I have now contributed over 500 such puzzles. Late in 2008 I received an email asking whether I would be interested in some of my crosswords being published in book form. My response was that I was very interested indeed, and here are the first 80 puzzles. All the quotations, unless stated otherwise in the puzzle, are taken from the King James Version of the Bible, on which the puzzles are loosely based. I hope you all have fun solving them.

Derek Banes

No 1

Across

5 St Augustine of _____ (5)
8 President of the council condemning Jesus (8)
9 Frequently (5)
10 Youngest son of Jacob and Rachel (8)
11 Seraph, perhaps (5)
14 Priest and prophet from Shiloh (3)
16 Judge of Israel who defeated the Midianite oppressors (6)
17 He denounced David for his abduction of Bathsheba (6)
18 Shortened form of 4 Down (3)
20 Jordan, for example (5)
24 It is forbidden by the second commandment (8)
25 Satan (5)
26 'I know that my _____ liveth' (Job 19:25) (8)
27 Affected with irritation (5)

Down

1 Crusts of dried blood (5)
2 4 Down had a close encounter with some of these (5)
3 Weapon used on Jesus during the crucifixion (5)
4 He interpreted the writing on the wall (6)
6 Numberless (8)
7 Belonging to the common people (8)
12 Earnest in application (8)
13 Prophet of doom (8)
14 Finish (3)
15 'There was no room for them in the ___ ' (Luke 2:7) (3)
19 Patron saint of Scotland (6)
21 Draw blood from (5)
22 Trample (5)
23 Gift of the magi (5)

No 2

Across

1 'Physician, heal _____ ' (Luke 4:23) (7)
5 Love affair (5)
8 Freight (5)
9 and 23 Saul consulted this medium (5,2,5)
10 Schoolmaster (7)
11 'I am Alpha and _____ ' (Revelation 1:8) (5)
12 Could a camel really pass through the eye of one? (6)
14 See 4 Down
17 Food provided for the Israelites in the wilderness (5)
19 Skin disease cured by Jesus (7)
22 Home of the recipients of one of Paul's epistles (7)
23 See 9 Across
24 Original name of the apostle Peter (5)
25 Orders of business (7)

Down

1 Unspoken (5)
2 Charge made for use of an enclosed space (7)
3 Father of Methusaleh (5)
4 and 14 Across 'Many are called but ___ ___ _____ '
(Matthew 22:14) (3,3,6)
5 Town in Syria mentioned in Acts and Galatians (7)
6 Red or yellow pigment (5)
7 Chorus (7)
12 Fourth book of the Pentateuch (7)
13 Connection (7)
15 Berated (7)
16 Old Testament prophet (6)
18 Book of the Old Testament (5)
20 Jesus was betrayed for thirty _____s of silver (5)
21 Stories (5)

No 3

Across

1 Take something offered (6)
4 Interpreted by Joseph in Genesis (5)
8 Musical instrument (5)
9 'Moab is my _____ : over Edom will I cast out my shoe' (Psalm 60:8) (7)
10 Relating to a town in Asia Minor, giving its name to a creed (7)
11 The apostle Paul went ashore here (Acts 21:3) (4)
12 To sin (3)
14 'Behold the ____ of God' (John 1:29) (4)
15 Old Testament book (4)
18 Body of water (3)
21 The devil proverbially finds work for these hands (4)
23 Staff carried by a bishop (7)
25 A name for the devil (7)
26 Larger version of 18 Across (5)
27 Holy and heavy are varieties of this (5)
28 Strikes (6)

Down

1 Climb (6)
2 Region visited by Paul, as mentioned in Galatians 1 (7)
3 Old Testament book ascribed to Solomon (8)
4 'Upon thy belly shalt thou go, and ____ shalt thou eat' (Genesis 3:14) (4)
5 Proverbially, these vessels make the most noise (5)
6 Relationship of the Virgin Mary to Jesus (6)
7 'Neither cast ye your pearls before _____ ' (Matthew 7:6) (5)
13 Hebrew king, son of Solomon (8)
16 Clothing (7)
17 Tree mentioned in Job 40 (6)
19 Fruit of the oak (5)
20 Twists (6)

Down (continued)

22 Legal (5)

24 Distant (4)

No 4

Across

1 'A time to kill, and a time to _____ ' (*Ecclesiastes 3:3*) (4)
3 This is forbidden by the seventh commandment (8)
9 Middle Eastern country mentioned in Matthew 4 (5)
10 Spirit said to wail before a death (7)
11 Vessel constructed by Noah (3)
13 Film had to be before you could see your photographs (9)
14 Cause to suffer for an offence (6)
16 Fibre twisted to form a rope (6)
18 Servility (9)
20 Created by God on the fourth day (3)
22 Large decorative wardrobe (7)
23 Set of beliefs, such as the Nicene Creed (5)
25 Exclamations of praise to God (8)
26 Alternative name for the apostle Matthew (4)

Down

1 Old Testament book (5)
2 Mixture of gases making up the earth's atmosphere (3)
4 'I am _____ both to the Greeks, and to the Barbarians' (*Romans 1:14*) (6)
5 Psalms is the _____ book of the Bible (7)
6 Recipients of an epistle from Paul (9)
7 Gave up (7)
8 Instrument played for Saul by David (4)
12 Alternative title for the Authorised Version of the Bible (4,5)
14 Egyptian ruler reluctant to release Moses (7)
15 A portion (7)
17 The children of _____ (*Ezra 2:53*) (6)
19 Upper part of a bottle (4)
21 Mother-in-law of Ruth (5)
24 The first woman (3)

No 5

Across

1 Be of service to (5)
4 Holy _____ , alternative form of Holy Ghost (6)
9 It is forbidden by the ninth commandment (7)
10 Ebbing and flowing (5)
11 Jacob's hirsute brother (4)
12 'Therefore he was their _____ ' (2 Samuel 23:19) (7)
13 Wednesday, the first day of Lent (3)
14 Son of Lot by his eldest daughter (Genesis 19:37) (4)
16 So be it (4)
18 Tune (3)
20 Angel of the pit (Revelation 9:11) (7)
21 Feng _____ , Chinese art of arranging furniture (4)
24 'For _____ is the kingdom' (Matthew 6:13) (5)
25 Old Testament book (7)
26 A Philistine city whose inhabitants are mentioned in Nehemiah 4 (6)
27 Stratum (5)

Down

1 'Comfort me with _____ ' (Song of Solomon 2:5) (6)
2 Major blood vessel (5)
3 Praise a 17th-century Archbishop of Canterbury (4)
5 High-ranking official in the Egyptian court, mentioned in Genesis (8)
6 Emit rays (7)
7 Old unit of weight or money (6)
8 Illegally judge and put to death (5)
13 Colleague of Shadrach and Meshach (8)
15 He set up a contest between Elijah and the prophets of Baal (7)
17 Sister of Mary and Lazarus (Luke 10:38) (6)
18 'Therefore was the king very wroth, and his _____ burned in him' (Esther 1:12) (5)
19 'And she became a _____ of salt' (Genesis 19:26) (6)

Down (continued)

22 Description of 11 Across (5)

23 Small room in which a monk might be found (4)

No 6

Across

1 Resting place of Noah's ark (6)
4 Epistle (6)
9 Luke, for example (7)
10 Deal with illness (5)
11 Direction from which the magi came to Jerusalem (4)
12 Progenitor, as Shem was of Abraham (8)
14 Jesus had one with the temple money changers (11)
18 Letters written to the Philippians and the Galatians (8)
20 Firstborn son of Shem (4)
22 'When Amnon's _____ is merry with wine' (2 Samuel 13:28) (5)
23 Persons confined in an institution (7)
24 'Behold, the man is _____ as one of us' (Genesis 3:22) (6)
25 Brand new (6)

Down

1 Grandson of Esau, son of Eliphaz and Timna (6)
2 Action of stimulating (7)
3 Deeds, as of the apostles (4)
5 Prayer (8)
6 It is forbidden by the eighth commandment (5)
7 'Set up the standard toward Zion: _____ , stay not' (Jeremiah 4:6) (6)
8 The angel of the Lord slew 185,000 of his men in one night (2 Kings 19:35) (11)
13 Small spinning top (8)
15 Persons dedicated to a monastic life, but not professed (7)
16 His son Malchiah repaired the Jerusalem wall (Nehemiah 3:14) (6)
17 Provoked mirth in (6)
19 Son of Abraham (5)
21 Portent (4)

No 7

Across

1 'Now will I lift up _____ ' (Isaiah 33:10) (6)
4 A line with sharp turns, alternately left and right (6)
7 Sea monster mentioned in Job 41 (9)
9 Instruments used for digging up weeds (4)
10 'For they have sown the wind, and they shall ____ the whirlwind' (Hosea 8:7) (4)
11 Staff of life (5)
13 Convent of monks or nuns subject to an abbey (6)
14 Something hired (6)
15 Mariner (6)
17 Issued by Caesar Augustus in Luke 2 (6)
19 Amos has been described as this type of prophet (5)
20 Saint blinded on the road to Damascus (4)
22 Insect mentioned in Matthew 23 (4)
23 Tomb (9)
24 A name for Satan (6)
25 He was raised by Eli the priest (6)

Down

1 Accident (6)
2 Abraham set seven of these aside in Genesis 21 (4)
3 Convent of a mendicant religious order (6)
4 Chamberlain of Ahasuerus in Esther 1 (6)
5 Equipment (4)
6 Narrative of the life of Christ (6)
7 Book of the Pentateuch (9)
8 Smooth-skinned peach (9)
11 Sweeping brush (5)
12 To frighten from (5)
15 Magnificent (6)
16 The manner of performing divine service (6)
17 Greek name for Tabitha in Acts 9 (6)

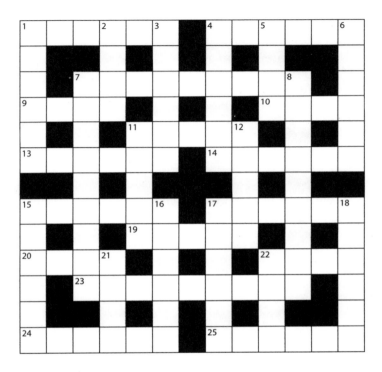

Down (continued)

18 To settle on a series of heirs (6)
21 Father of Gershon, Kohath and Merari in Genesis 46 (4)
22 Forbidding (4)

No 8

Across

3 The Eucharist, for example (9)
8 'Neither shall there be any more _____ ' (Revelation 21:4) (4)
9 Characteristic of the Church of England (8)
10 You may do this to your brain to solve a puzzle! (6)
13 Not used in unleavened bread (5)
14 Make use of (7)
15 Its jawbone was used as a weapon by Samson (3)
16 Metric measure of area (7)
17 Saint who has a cathedral in Moscow (5)
21 Hotel room for sitting or waiting (6)
22 An agreement entered into, such as between God and Noah (8)
23 A furious driver, named after one of the kings of Israel (4)
24 Whitsuntide (9)

Down

1 Books of the Bible not accepted as such by Protestants (9)
2 Obstacle (9)
4 Gemstones (5)
5 Larvae of flies (7)
6 'To give us a _____ in his holy place' (Ezra 9:8) (4)
7 Grandson of Esau and son of Eliphaz in Genesis 36 (4)
11 Nonconformist (9)
12 Supposed god worshipped by the Philistines (9)
14 Put to some purpose (3)
15 Language widely spoken in the Middle East in biblical times (7)
18 Female choristers having the lowest voices (5)
19 'Let me pull out the _____ out of thine eye' (Matthew 7:4) (4)
20 The time from Ash Wednesday to Easter (4)

No 9

Across

1 Blind beggar mentioned in Mark 10 (10)
8 An early evening meal including a hot dish (4,3)
9 According to Proverbs 16:18, it 'goeth before destruction' (5)
10 'The cucumbers, and the melons, and the _____s, and the onions, and the garlick' (Numbers 11:5) (4)
11 Mother of Jesus (4)
12 His wife was turned to a pillar of salt (3)
14 Adjective describing Samson (6)
15 Precious metal of which talents could be made (6)
18 Son of Ikkesh in 2 Samuel 23 (3)
20 Weed found among the wheat in Matthew 13 (4)
21 Scheme (4)
23 'The captive _____ hasteneth' (Isaiah 51:14) (5)
24 Son of Joseph and brother of Manasseh (7)
25 Incapable of error (10)

Down

1 An object of annoyance (7)
2 Daughter-in-law of Naomi (4)
3 Old Testament book and prophet (6)
4 Cause of death when body tissues are starved of oxygen (8)
5 Son of Tahath in 1 Chronicles 6 (5)
6 Israel's perennial enemies (11)
7 Book of the Pentateuch (11)
13 Solemn ecclesiastical curse (8)
16 Latin version of the scriptures (7)
17 Distressing experience (6)
19 'I am an _____ in their sight' (Job 19:15) (5)
22 King of Israel 874–853BC (4)

No 10

Across

5 Son of Abraham (5)
8 Book containing an account of the rebuilding of the walls of Jerusalem (8)
9 Material of which Goliath's helmet was made (5)
10 Pertaining to a bishop's jurisdiction (8)
11 Allow to fall (5)
14 Courteous title for a gentleman (3)
16 Old Testament book and prophet (6)
17 Mount of _____ Hill near Jerusalem (6)
18 Land of ___ , proverbial place of sleep (3)
20 Composition (5)
24 Angelic beings ranking below 6 Down (8)
25 'We may eat of the _____' (*Genesis* 3:2) (5)
26 Bishop's throne (8)
27 Disease suffered by Aeneas in Acts 9 (5)

Down

1 Positive electrode (5)
2 Disorder (5)
3 'As the colour of _____' (*Ezekiel* 1:4) (5)
4 Member of a Muslim sect (6)
6 Angelic beings ranking above 24 Across (8)
7 Given absolution (8)
12 Coastal town to the north-west of Jerusalem (8)
13 _____ Loyola, founder of the Jesuits (8)
14 Moral offence (3)
15 Moses had one of these, as did Aaron (3)
19 Son of Meonothai in 1 Chronicles 4 (6)
21 Prefix meaning 'perpendicular' (5)
22 ' _____ with me', a popular hymn (5)
23 Capital of modern-day Jordan (5)

No 11

Across

1 Fancy cake (6)
4 Extremely distressing (6)
7 Birthplace of Jesus (9)
9 Goliath's height was six cubits and one of these (4)
10 Adjective often used to describe Mary (4)
11 The river flowed with it in Exodus 7 (5)
13 'In the _____ of one Tyrannus' (Acts 19:9) (6)
14 To wish otherwise (6)
15 '_____ the beauty of the Lord' (Psalm 27:4) (6)
17 Eros, for example (6)
19 Subdivisions of a religion (5)
20 Gown (4)
22 A gift of the magi (4)
23 '_____ of the Magi', a popular subject for painters (9)
24 Doctrines laid down with authority (6)
25 Saintlier (6)

Down

1 'Her _____ are in the depths of hell' (Proverbs 9:18) (6)
2 Garden home of Adam and Eve (4)
3 As is the way to the top of Mount Carmel (6)
4 Less serious form of the geological upheaval mentioned in Amos 1 (6)
5 Interjection used to gain attention (4)
6 Believe (6)
7 Wife of Uriah the Hittite (9)
8 The Exodus, for example (9)
11 The Egyptians were cursed with these in Exodus 9 (5)
12 'Forgive us our _____ ' (Matthew 6:12) (5)
15 Entombed (6)
16 Wreckage (6)
17 Sew (6)

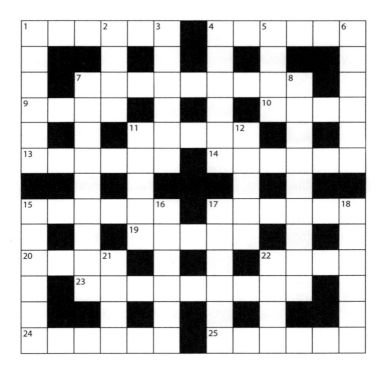

Down (continued)

18 Make beloved (6)
21 Ancient country between the Dead Sea and the Gulf of Aqaba (4)
22 Target (4)

No 12

Across

1 Belt fastening (6)
4 Original name of Abraham (5)
8 Tree of the olive family (5)
9 Son of Abraham (7)
10 Ban on trade (7)
11 Said to indicate one has enough 3 Down? (4)
12 Father of Joshua (3)
14 One of a pair of objects used as an oracle in Exodus (4)
15 The first murder victim (4)
18 'He planteth an ___ , and the rain doth nourish it' (Isaiah 44:14) (3)
21 Flower mentioned in Isaiah 35 (4)
23 'But let a man _____ himself' (1 Corinthians 11:28) (7)
25 Address (5,2)
26 Son of Cain (5)
27 Coastal town mentioned in Mark 7 (5)
28 Tool used in the construction of the ark? (6)

Down

1 Faith (6)
2 Diameter of gun barrel (US spelling) (7)
3 _____ Christi, a type of wine (8)
4 Dull pain (4)
5 'They _____ even to the sea of Jazer' (Jeremiah 48:32) (5)
6 Fruits mentioned in Numbers 11 (6)
7 Father of Judas Iscariot (5)
13 Town where Jesus grew up (8)
16 They prepare work for publication (7)
17 Has faith (6)
19 King of Judea 37–34BC (5)
20 Jacob dreamed of his ladder here (6)
22 'He would not _____ the time in Asia' (Acts 20:16) (5)
24 'I am escaped with the _____ of my teeth' (Job 19:20) (4)

No 13

Across

7 Cover for optic organ (6)
8 'Hark! The _____ angels sing' (6)
10 Extent of a bishop's jurisdiction (7)
11 To dig (archaic) (5)
12 Father of Ham, Shem and Japheth (4)
13 Food provided in the wilderness (5)
17 Garment worn by priests in the Old Testament (5)
18 Plant used in cookery, often mentioned in Genesis (4)
22 Book of the Old Testament (5)
23 Having no purpose (7)
24 Antelopes (6)
25 Swiss city giving its name to a version of the Bible (6)

Down

1 Remaining undecided (7)
2 Only woman to be a judge in ancient Israel (7)
3 Those of Jacob were Leah and Rachel (5)
4 Celebration of holy matrimony (7)
5 Crypt with an arched roof or ceiling (5)
6 Snake mentioned in Psalm 58 (5)
9 The Ten Commandments (9)
14 Direction taken to reach the summit of Mount Sinai (7)
15 Father of the apostles James and John (7)
16 Shunammite woman who served David as a nurse (7)
19 Number of times 21 Down denied Jesus before cockcrow (5)
20 The Muslim religion (5)
21 Apostle reputedly martyred at the hands of Nero (5)

No 14

Across

1 'Neither shalt thou gather every _____ ' (*Leviticus 19:10*) (5)
4 He led the Israelites out of Egypt (5)
10 Taper (5)
11 David restrained him from killing King Saul (7)
12 _____ da Vinci (8)
13 Home town of 25 Across (4)
15 Brother of 4 Across (5)
17 These creatures bred in manna saved overnight (5)
21 'The Pharisees began to _____ him' (*Luke 11:53*) (4)
22 Common description of a bride (8)
25 Philistine giant killed by David (7)
26 Its making is forbidden by the second commandment (5)
27 Sharp (5)
28 Holy city of Islam (5)

Down

2 Animal with nasal horn (*abb.*) (5)
3 and 24 14 Down was turned into one (6,2,4)
5 Leave out (4)
6 A grandson of Jacob and brother of Manasseh (7)
7 Part of the 19th book of the Old Testament (5)
8 'Now therefore restore those _____ again' (*Judges 11:13*) (5)
9 Saul was blinded by this in Acts 9 (5)
14 She looked back at Sodom (4,4)
16 In the manner of a seraph, for example (7)
18 ' _____ me with hyssop' (*Psalm 51:7*) (5)
19 He was angry with Job in Job 32 (5)
20 White heron (5)
23 Son of Abraham and Sarah (5)

No 15

Across

1 Saint, father of the Virgin Mary (7)
5 Uniform jacket (5)
8 'Paul was suffered to _____ by himself' (Acts 28:16) (5)
9 Paul wrote two epistles to him (7)
10 'I will _____ the graving thereof' (Zechariah 3:9) (7)
11 Retook an examination (5)
12 'The ____ __ my shepherd' (Psalm 23:1) (4,2)
14 Such tributes are often seen at funerals (6)
17 Indian princes (5)
19 State of the apostle Thomas? (2,5)
22 Atone for sin (7)
23 Leader of the tribe of Zebulun in Numbers 1 (5)
24 The bread baked by Lot in Genesis 19 contained none of this (5)
25 Fourth book of the Bible (7)

Down

1 Leader of Israel before the establishment of the monarchy (5)
2 'The Lord is the _____ ' (1 Thessalonians 4:6) (7)
3 Board game (5)
4 Relationship of Sarah to Isaac (6)
5 Musical instrument played by Miriam in Exodus 15 (7)
6 Paper money (5)
7 Fifteenth wedding anniversary (7)
12 It is forbidden by the eighth commandment (7)
13 'Yea, it shall be at an _____ suddenly' (Isaiah 29:5) (7)
15 Join again (7)
16 He blessed Mary and Joseph in Luke 2 (6)
18 Town where Jonah took ship to Tarshish (5)
20 Martin Luther King spoke of having one (5)
21 Pipes (5)

No 16

Across

5 Land attached to a parish church (5)
8 It is forbidden by the sixth commandment (8)
9 Cousin of King Saul in 1 Samuel 14 (5)
10 Celebration in progress when Jesus performed the miracle at Cana (8)
11 Missile thrown at adulteresses, among others (5)
14 'With his ___ he smote the rock' (*Numbers 20:11*) (3)
16 Convent subject to an abbey (6)
17 Harlot symbolic of Samaria in Ezekiel 23 (6)
18 Lowering of the tide (3)
20 Counterfeit (5)
24 Survivor of the fiery furnace (8)
25 'Keep _____ and judgment' (*Hosea 12:6*) (5)
26 Begs (8)
27 Undress, like Aaron in Numbers 20 (5)

Down

1 A set of bells (5)
2 'He that is surety for a stranger shall _____ for it' (*Proverbs 11:15*) (5)
3 A pilgrim's pouch (5)
4 Slowly (*musical*) (6)
6 Pouring of wine in honour of God (8)
7 Every two years (8)
12 Part of church at right angles to the nave (8)
13 Adoptive father of Esther (8)
14 Cereal crop (3)
15 Small flatfish (3)
19 'The child Jesus tarried _____ in Jerusalem' (*Luke 2:43*) (6)
21 'That they may _____ the doctrine of God' (*Titus 2:10*) (5)
22 Father of Leah and Rachel (5)
23 Large box, such as the ark of the covenant (5)

No 17

Across

1   Sentry (5)
4   Jesus raised him from the dead (7)
8   Lake by whose shores certain scrolls were found (4,3)
9   'Let him be your _____ ' (Isaiah 8:13) (5)
10 Eskimo dwelling (5)
11 Religion established in the 16th century by former Hindus (7)
13 'Are they the _____ of Abraham?' (2 Corinthians 11:22) (4)
15 Wife of Jacob (6)
17 Source, derivation (6)
20 Distance mentioned in Matthew 5 (4)
22 'Lord, remember me when thou comest into thy _____ '
    (Luke 23:42) (7)
24 From which butter is made (5)
26 Bailiff (5)
27 A sugar (7)
28 Stinging plants (7)
29 Moral significance (5)

Down

1   More pious (7)
2   To benefit (5)
3   Ordain what is to be (7)
4   Form a link with (6)
5   Priest mentioned in 2 Samuel 8 (5)
6   Smoking (7)
7   One of the cities of the plains (5)
12 One of 21 Down (4)
14 Alternative name for St Erasmus (4)
16 Change from one religion to another (7)
18 Hermit (7)
19 Old Testament book (7)
21 Their making is forbidden by the second commandment (6)

Down (continued)

22 Muslim scriptures (5)

23 'They that _____ in the land' *(Isaiah 9:2)* (5)

25 Father of Methuselah (5)

No 18

Across

1 Thong (5)
8 Wife of Ananias in Acts 5 (8)
9 Fluid contained in a font (5)
10 'And all that believed were _____ ' (Acts 2:44) (8)
11 Colouring material (5)
12 Name sometimes applied to a large lake, such as that of Galilee (3)
16 Old Testament book (6)
17 Church office (Philippians 1:1) (6)
18 Land to which Cain fled (3)
23 Garment worn by monks (5)
24 Member of Jewish religious party at the time of Jesus (8)
25 Religious service by night (5)
26 One who breaks the second commandment (8)
27 One of the plagues called down on Egypt by Moses (5)

Down

2 Violent person (8)
3 Companion of Shadrach and Meshach (8)
4 She demanded the head of John the Baptist (6)
5 Church recesses (5)
6 'There shined round about him a _____ from heaven' (Acts 9:3) (5)
7 An army chaplain (5)
12 Moral offence (3)
13 Compute the sum of (3)
14 Paul was educated at his feet (Acts 22:3) (8)
15 Crime of which Cain was guilty (8)
19 'And when he had _____ the seventh seal' (Revelation 8:1) (6)
20 'When they divide the _____ ' (Isaiah 9:3) (5)
21 Fruit of the locust-tree (5)
22 Essential (5)

No 19

Across

1   Father-in-law of David in 2 Samuel 3 (6)
5   Writer of documents for others (6)
8   Prickly plants (8)
9   Tug (4)
10 Italian sparkling wine (4)
11 Vague, formless (8)
13 King of Judah 872–848BC (11)
15 Snag (8)
17 'God will provide himself a ____ ' (*Genesis 22:8*) (4)
19 Shortened name of New Testament book (4)
20 Washes (8)
21 Detective created by Agatha Christie (6)
22 Tool used for cutting grass (6)

Down

2   Accompaniment to sackcloth? (5)
3   Expected deliverer of the Jews (7)
4   Such as the Dead? (6,3)
5   Former international distress signal (1,1,1)
6   'Once in ____ David's city' (5)
7   Belshazzar's feast could be described as one (7)
12 Periods of unconsciousness (9)
13 City conquered by Joshua (7)
14 Good Friday, for instance (7)
16 Even shrewder than Solomon? (5)
18 Substance used to perfume a bed in Proverbs 7 (5)
20 His wife looked back (3)

No 20

Across

1 Read in a casual manner (6)
4 Jesus (6)
7 Trade of the apostles James and John (9)
9 Filth (4)
10 Ancient gambling cubes (4)
11 Prefix denoting 'English' (5)
14 The devil (5)
15 Deluge survived by Noah and his family (5)
16 'Acquainted with _____ ' (Isaiah 53:3) (5)
17 To blaspheme (5)
18 'To _____ thing there is a season' (Ecclesiastes 3:1) (5)
20 Horseman (5)
23 Bellow (4)
25 Luxuriant (4)
26 There were many of these after the tower of Babel (9)
27 'Go and sit down in the _____ room' (Luke 14:10) (6)
28 Prophet who ascended to heaven in a chariot of fire (6)

Down

1 Centres of attention at weddings (6)
2 Week beginning on the seventh Sunday after Easter (4)
3 The son of Kishi in 1 Chronicles 6 (5)
4 Christmas song (5)
5 'The staff of this bruised _____ ' (2 Kings 18:21) (4)
6 'This line of scarlet _____ ' (Joshua 2:18) (6)
7 Aaron's relationship to Moses (9)
8 He helped Joseph of Arimathea to entomb Jesus (9)
11 Jesus was moved to this emotion by the money changers (5)
12 Work a mill, as Samson did in prison (5)
13 Tender (5)
17 Elijah met the prophets of Baal on this mountain (6)
19 Alternative name of Jehovah (6)

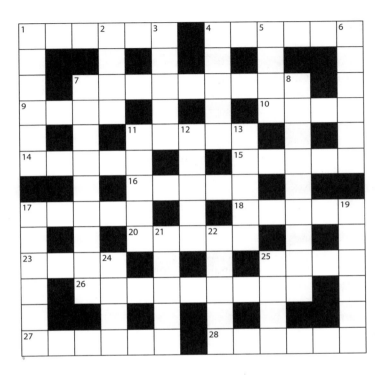

Down (continued)

21 Mass of unwrought metal (5)

22 Rub out (5)

24 Tool probably not used in the garden of Eden (4)

25 Third son of Jacob by Leah (4)

No 21

Across

1   Call on divine power to cause harm (5)
4   Counting frame possibly used in biblical times (6)
9   William Caxton, for example (7)
10 'For he shall be like the ____ in the desert' (*Jeremiah 17:6*) (5)
11 Alternative name for Esau (4)
12 Retributive justice (7)
13 Insect mentioned in Proverbs 6 (3)
14 Animal used as a burnt offering by Samuel in 1 Samuel 7 (4)
16 Strong city in Joshua 19 (4)
18 The first Wednesday in Lent (3)
20 Precious stone mentioned in chapter 28 of 25 Across (7)
21 Follow orders (4)
24 Son of Aaron by Elisheba (*Exodus 6:23*) (5)
25 Old Testament book and prophet (7)
26 Weapon made by Ehud in Judges 3 (6)
27 Backpacked (5)

Down

1   'And two vessels of fine _____ ' (*Ezra 8:27*) (6)
2   Pertaining to the nose (*prefix*) (5)
3   Consumes (4)
5   Huge beast described in Job 40 (8)
6   Less fine (7)
7   Breach in church unity (6)
8   ' _____ him mercy in the sight of this man' (*Nehemiah 1:11*) (5)
13 Free from limits (8)
15 ' _____ grace' (7)
17 Masculine forename (6)
18 Snake described as deaf in Psalm 58 (5)
19 Facial feature mentioned in Job 16 (6)
22 The Israelites were forced to make this without straw (5)
23 First wife of Jacob (4)

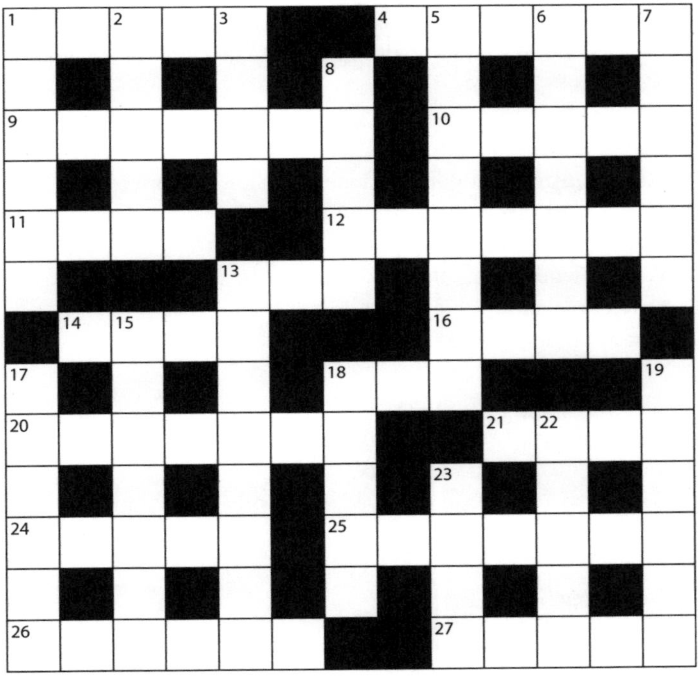

No 22

Across

1   Probably not the dance performed by the daughter of Herodias in Matthew 14 (5)
4   Cuthbert is their patron saint (7)
8   Halves (7)
9   Musical instrument not mentioned in Daniel 3 (5)
10 Spiky desert plants (5)
11 Smoking (7)
13 Wealthy landowner who married Ruth (4)
15 Brother of Simon Peter (6)
17 Sister of Leah and wife of Jacob (6)
20 Son of Lamech (4)
22 'Who hath _____ of eyes?' (*Proverbs 23:29*) (7)
24 Son of Abraham and Sarah (5)
26 Weapon mentioned in Jeremiah 50 (5)
27 Descriptive of the living enjoyed by the prodigal son in Luke 15 (7)
28 'All the _____ in ships' (*Revelation 18:17*) (7)
29 Encounters (5)

Down

1   Mother of Jacob and Esau, as spelt in Romans 9 (7)
2   Played by David on the harp (5)
3   ' _____ ye greatness unto our God' (*Deuteronomy 32:3*) (7)
4   Canaanite commander killed by Jael (6)
5   That of Abraham included Zimran and Jokshan (*Genesis 25:2*) (5)
6   Large bird in Job 39 (7)
7   Raise the shoulders (5)
12 Old Testament book (4)
14 Possesses (4)
16 'O ye travelling companies of _____ ' (*Isaiah 21:13*) (7)
18 Wife of David and mother of Amnon (2 *Samuel 3:2*) (7)
19 One of the plagues of Egypt (7)

Down (continued)

21 Bird of prey mentioned in Deuteronomy 14 (*up-to-date spelling*) (6)

22 Personal memorial of a saint, held in reverence (5)

23 Fluid injected into the rectum (5)

25 Make reparation for sin (5)

No 23

Across

1 Serious crime (6)
4 'And the river _____ ' (Exodus 7:21) (5)
8 Precious stone mentioned in Ezekiel 28 (5)
9 Shortest book of the Old Testament (7)
10 Whip such as that used on Jesus before crucifixion (7)
11 Seven weeks after Easter (abb.) (4)
12 Joan of ___ (3)
14 Abnormal lump on the body (4)
15 Daughter-in-law of Naomi (4)
18 Son of Noah (3)
21 'They cried out all at _____ ' (Luke 23:18) (4)
23 One who has got away (7)
25 Of the heart (7)
26 One of the plagues of Egypt (5)
27 Weapon used by David to kill Goliath (5)
28 A going out, as the Israelites from Egypt (6)

Down

1 Something regarded with irrational reverence (6)
2 Disease cured by Jesus (7)
3 Home town of Jesus (8)
4 'And to _____ up the vision' (Daniel 9:24) (4)
5 US religious sect (5)
6 Son of Levi in Genesis 46 (6)
7 God commanded him to marry the prostitute Gomer (5)
13 Cross (8)
16 A fever (7)
17 Woman who did good works in Acts 9 (6)
19 Holy city of Islam (5)
20 Official enumeration of inhabitants (6)
22 Dog favoured by the British royal family (5)
24 The Fisherman's _____ , as worn by the Pope (4)

No 24

Across

1 Lie about lazily (4)
5 'Plenty of _____ and wine' (*Genesis 27:28*) (4)
7 Wife of Nabal and later David (7)
8 Festival celebrated on 6 January (8)
10 Precious stone mentioned in Proverbs 31 (4)
12 Ring around the head of a holy person (4)
14 Ninth son of Jacob and fifth son of Leah (8)
16 Christened (8)
17 Period of fasting preceding Easter (4)
18 Inhabitant of the former Siam (4)
19 Active ingredient in toothpaste (8)
22 Gathering of crops celebrated by a church festival (7)
23 It contains water with which one is 16 Across (4)
24 'And when _____ was now come' (*John 6:16*) (4)

Down

1 One of the plagues of Egypt (4)
2 Ten virgins each took one of these in Matthew 25 (4)
3 Prayers of supplication (8)
4 Type of chapel dedicated to the Virgin Mary (4)
5 Type of collar worn by the vicar (8)
6 Fleet such as that of Hiram in 1 Kings 10 (4)
9 Ruler of Egypt at the time of Moses (7)
11 David did this to Goliath (7)
13 Absolute (8)
15 Member of Jewish party in opposition to the Pharisees (8)
18 To cover with grass (4)
19 'Offered strange _____ before the Lord' (*Leviticus 10:1*) (4)
20 Ceremonial form of observance, especially religious (4)
21 Garden home of Adam (4)

No 25

Across

1 'Let us lay _____ every weight' (Hebrews 12:1) (5)
4 Father of Methuselah (5)
10 Protective garment (7)
11 Serviceable (2,3)
12 Christian descendants of the ancient Egyptians (5)
13 Followers of one branch of Islam (7)
15 'But knowledge is _____ unto him that understandeth' (Proverbs 14:6) (4)
17 Disciple who betrayed Christ (5)
19 Boaz's heart was this in Ruth 3 (5)
22 Ruler such as Jeroboam I (4)
25 Cover with a hard coating (7)
27 Prayer said before meals (5)
29 Shed blood (5)
30 Abraham did this in Genesis 17 (7)
31 A recording in a book of accounts (5)
32 'Thou shalt not lend upon _____ ' (Deuteronomy 23:19) (5)

Down

2 Slumber, as Jacob did at Bethel (5)
3 Lake with high concentration of mineral salts (4,3)
5 Widow of Elimelech (5)
6 'My beloved is unto me as a _____ of camphire' (Song of Solomon 1:14) (7)
7 That of a pilgrim is a scrip (5)
8 Revelation 4 mentions a sea of this substance (5)
9 Subdivision of a chapter of the Bible (5)
14 Song of praise (4)
16 Inquires (4)
18 The swine is such an animal, according to Leviticus 11 (7)
20 Food mentioned in Job 6 could be eaten from these (7)
21 Those eaten in Exodus 12 are bitter (5)

Down (continued)

23 Paul died in the city which is the capital of this country (5)
24 Plants wrapped around Jonah's head (5)
26 Below (5)
28 'Thou shalt not _____ an Edomite' (*Deuteronomy 23:7*) (5)

No 26

Across

7 Consecrate with oil (6)
8 By mouth (6)
10 St Peter, for example (7)
11 He led the Israelites out of Egypt (5)
12 The bedstead of King Og of Bashan was made of this
   (*Deuteronomy 3:11*) (4)
13 Colour of the asses mentioned in Judges 5 (5)
17 Abel was a keeper of these animals (5)
18 Bird released three times from Noah's ark (4)
22 'The price of wisdom is _____ rubies' (*Job 28:18*) (5)
23 'Neither give heed to fables and _____ genealogies'
   (*1 Timothy 1:4*) (7)
24 Old Testament book (6)
25 'The _____ and morning star' (*Revelation 22:16*) (6)

Down

1 Capital of the northern kingdom of Israel (7)
2 King of Israel renowned for his wisdom (7)
3 'Dwell together in _____ ' (*Psalm 133:1*) (5)
4 Archbishop in charge of a province (7)
5 Consecrate (5)
6 Romany (5)
9 Birthplace of Jesus (9)
14 Violators of the eighth commandment (7)
15 Alien (7)
16 Degree of compactness (7)
19 First bird released from Noah's ark (5)
20 Forward (*archaic*) (5)
21 'O come, let us _____ him' (*Adeste Fidelis*) (5)

No 27

Across

1 Relating to Pentecost (7)
5 Inheritors of the earth? (4)
7 Garden flower (5)
8 Place where Jacob dreamt of a ladder (6)
10 'Repent of this _____ ' *(Exodus 32:12)* (4)
11 Philosophy of Zeno's followers (8)
13 A son of David in 2 Samuel 5 (6)
14 Precious stone mentioned in Revelation 4 (6)
17 Household employees such as those of Pharaoh in Exodus 9 (8)
19 Descriptive of the land around the Dead Sea (4)
21 Card serving as token of admission (6)
22 'Go and get thee a _____ girdle' *(Jeremiah 13:1)* (5)
23 Look for (4)
24 'Not willing to make her a publick _____ ' *(Matthew 1:19)* (7)

Down

1 Desolate wasteland where Jesus fasted for 40 days (10)
2 That of Jesus' face is said to be on the Turin Shroud (7)
3 A psalm is a devotional one (4)
4 Owner of a vineyard in 1 Kings 21 (6)
5 Fabulous (8)
6 Fragrant resin obtained from various tropical trees (5)
9 Opposite of a virtue that dwells with wisdom in Proverbs 8 (10)
12 Old Testament prophet and book (8)
15 Root crop (7)
16 Sculpture (6)
18 'Then shall we _____ against him' *(Micah 5:5)* (5)
20 Insect sought by the king of Israel in 1 Samuel 26 (4)

No 28

Across

1 Allow to enter (5)
4 One of the apostles (6)
9 Musician such as David (7)
10 More agreeable (5)
11 Mark from which darts are thrown (4)
12 Book of the Pentateuch (7)
13 Vessel built by Noah (3)
14 Son of Noah (4)
16 Columba founded a monastery on this island (4)
18 Land to which Cain fled (3)
20 'And I will _____ to you the years' (Joel 2:25) (7)
21 'Ye ____ up also the wheat' (Matthew 13:29) (4)
24 Leader of a synagogue (5)
25 Language probably spoken by Jesus (7)
26 Bicycle made for two (6)
27 'Thou shalt not sow thy vineyard with divers _____ ' (Deuteronomy 22:9) (5)

Down

1 Philistine city mentioned in 1 Samuel 5 (6)
2 Aromatic gum given to the baby Jesus (5)
3 The lilies of the field do not do this (4)
5 Hagar was this sort of servant to Sarai in Genesis 16 (8)
6 From which lessons are read in church (7)
7 'And ye shall _____ among the heathen' (Leviticus 26:38) (6)
8 Smelt, like manna left until morning in Exodus 16 (5)
13 Member of tribe mentioned in 1 Samuel 11 (8)
15 City built by the children of Reuben in Numbers 32 (7)
17 Mountain on which the ark landed (6)
18 Father of King Jeroboam (1 Kings 11:26) (5)
19 Jeremiah was placed in this confining device (6)
22 Make a speech (5)
23 Religious service (4)

No 29

Across

1   'John had his raiment of camel's _____ ' (*Matthew 3:4*) (4)
3   Town at which Paul landed in Acts 18 (8)
9   Fashion (5)
10 Woman full of good works in Acts 9 (7)
11 King of Judah 910–869BC (3)
13 Performed with exaggeration (9)
14 Lozenge shapes (6)
16 'The devil had _____ him in the midst' (*Luke 4:35*) (6)
18 Wife of Uriah the Hittite (9)
20 Relationship of Shem to Noah (3)
22 Hostility (3-4)
23 Due (5)
25 'The _____ also with the man of gray hairs'
    (*Deuteronomy 32:25*) (8)
26 'And when they did _____ it with an omer' (*Exodus 16:18*) (4)

Down

1   Prophet who married Gomer, a prostitute (5)
2   Climbing plant mentioned in the title of a popular carol (3)
4   'Zadok the priest', for example (6)
5   The fourth commandment tells us to remember this day (7)
6   Revolutions (9)
7   Relinquish (7)
8   Roman emperor who persecuted Christians (4)
12 Pertaining to St Peter, perhaps (9)
14 Burrowing animals (7)
15 Like an animal (7)
17 German city (6)
19 Prophet and Old Testament book (4)
21 Son of Maath in Luke 3 (5)
24 'Which are blackish by reason of the ___ ' (*Job 6:16*) (3)

No 30

Across

1 From which the sermon is preached (6)
4 Object having interest by reason of its age (5)
8 English cathedral city (5)
9 Ceremonially impure (7)
10 Foolish (7)
11 Continent in which Bethlehem is situated (4)
12 A son of Noah (3)
14 Type of melon (4)
15 'An ____ to bind his soul' (Numbers 30:2) (4)
18 The Creator (3)
21 'They have ____ wheat' (Jeremiah 12:13) (4)
23 Sceptical, like Thomas (2,5)
25 'And they shall eat up thine _____ ' (Jeremiah 5:17) (7)
26 Heavenly body, possibly like that followed by the magi (5)
27 13 Down wore such apparel in Esther 8 (5)
28 Boil gently (6)

Down

1 She laboured much in the Lord according to Romans 16 (6)
2 Bird mentioned in Leviticus 11 (7)
3 Setting fire to (8)
4 Upon which a wise man built his house in Matthew 7 (4)
5 Vegetables mentioned in Numbers 11 (5)
6 Grandson of Noah (6)
7 'And ye shall take a ____ of hyssop' (Exodus 12:22) (5)
13 Adoptive father of 17 Down (8)
16 One of a pair of objects used as an oracle in Exodus (7)
17 Old Testament book and woman's name (6)
19 'That that ____ , let it die' (Zechariah 11:9) (5)
20 Ancient Greek coin (6)
22 Pester (5)
24 Source of water mentioned in Genesis 49 (4)

No 31

Across

1 Colour of the horses going north in Zechariah 6 (5)
4 'Coming out of the _____ ' (*Matthew* 8:28) (5)
10 The Japanese art of flower arranging (7)
11 'Depart not _____ , I pray thee' (*Judges* 6:18) (5)
12 Vietnamese capital city (5)
13 Shunammite woman mentioned in 1 Kings 1 (7)
15 Town where Jesus turned water into wine (4)
17 Location of a proposed tower to heaven (5)
19 Jacob's second son by Zilpah (5)
22 Condiment mentioned in 2 Kings 2 (4)
25 'And will cause to cease the _____ ' (*Hosea* 1:4) (7)
27 Number of chapters in the Song of Solomon (5)
29 Bird of prey mentioned in Habakkuk 1 (5)
30 Most excellent (7)
31 'It hath no _____ ' (*Hosea* 8:7) (5)
32 Cost of a measure of wheat in Revelation 6 (5)

Down

2 Remain in bed longer than usual (3,2)
3 Cup used for Communion (7)
5 One of the twelve cities of Benjamin in Joshua 18 (5)
6 Irish spirit said to wail before a death (7)
7 'Turn aside the poor in the gate from their _____ ' (*Amos* 5:12) (5)
8 Father of Leah and Rachel (5)
9 That of Solomon lasted from 970 to 930BC (5)
14 God of the Canaanites (4)
16 In addition (4)
18 After dark (2,5)
20 A church spire (7)
21 'The _____ sent out a sound' (*Psalm* 77:17) (5)
23 Nephew of King David, killed by Joab (5)
24 Give voice to (5)

Down (continued)

26 Reside (5)

28 To gather corn like Ruth (5)

No 32

Across

5 Tool used for digging (5)
8 Stories told by Jesus to illustrate moral points (8)
9 Hasten (5)
10 Ur of the _____ (8)
11 Vegetables brought by Barzillai in 2 Samuel 17 (5)
14 Diocese (3)
16 Governor of Judea at the time of the crucifixion (6)
17 Insect sent to plague Egypt (6)
18 Attempt (3)
20 Two of these were released from the ark before the flood receded (5)
24 Survivor of the fiery furnace (8)
25 'In the whirlwind and in the _____ ' (Nahum 1:3) (5)
26 One of a Canaanite tribe mentioned in Genesis 10 (8)
27 Fetch (5)

Down

1 A small particle (5)
2 Joseph interpreted that of Pharaoh (5)
3 'Mary _____ with her' (Luke 1:56) (5)
4 Worship (6)
6 'He hath abounded toward us in all wisdom and _____ ' (Ephesians 1:8) (8)
7 'And _____ was upon the face of the deep' (Genesis 1:2) (8)
12 Member of the clergy (8)
13 A small orange (8)
14 Solidify (3)
15 English cathedral city (3)
19 The price of a virtuous woman is said to be above these (6)
21 'An _____ of a sweet smell' (Philippians 4:18) (5)
22 Danger (5)
23 Strength or energy (5)

No 33

Across

1 Colour associated with Dominican friars (5)
4 Church congregation (5)
10 A _____ , unaccompanied singing (7)
11 'If he smite out his manservant's _____ ' *(Exodus 21:27)* (5)
12 Original name of Abraham (5)
13 Abdon had thirty such relatives in Judges 12 (7)
15 Husband of Ruth (4)
17 Song of thanksgiving or triumph (5)
19 Pontius Pilate, for example (5)
22 'Bread for all their cattle for that _____ ' *(Genesis 47:17)* (4)
25 'He shall lie all night _____ my breasts' *(Song of Solomon 1:13)* (7)
27 Disciple also called Simon (5)
29 Small role in play or film (5)
30 Liar in Acts 5 (7)
31 'Two lions standing by the _____ ' *(2 Chronicles 9:18)* (5)
32 A chapter of the 19th book of the Old Testament (5)

Down

2 For example, Naaman in 2 Kings 5 (5)
3 Saint, missionary to Scotland (7)
5 Abate (3,2)
6 Infectious disease (7)
7 Small fragment (5)
8 Food provided for the Israelites in the wilderness (5)
9 Abyss (5)
14 Son of Seraiah, after whom an Old Testament book is named (4)
16 Precious stone mentioned in Ezekiel 28 (4)
18 Try (7)
20 'We are _____ and fatherless' *(Lamentations 5:3)* (7)
21 Of sails, pressed back against the mast (5)
23 The Israelites camped here in Exodus 13 (5)

Down (continued)

24 Upon which Jesus was crucified (5)
26 Material of which beds were made in Amos 6 (5)
28 'He will laugh at the _____ of the innocent' (Job 9:23) (5)

No 34

Across

1 Food mentioned in Obadiah (5)
4 Metalworkers in Jeremiah 29 (6)
9 Angel (7)
10 First month, according to Esther 3 (5)
11 Totals (4)
12 'Thou art an _____ man' (*Luke 19:21*) (7)
13 Father of Joshua (3)
14 Footwear in Joshua 5 (4)
16 Reflection of sound (4)
18 'No ___ can come between them' (*Job 41:16*) (3)
20 Cells of a church containing their own altars (7)
21 Woodwind instrument (4)
24 Brother of Goliath in 1 Chronicles 20 (5)
25 Major prophet of the Old Testament (7)
26 Small open boat (6)
27 Mother of Ishmael in Genesis 16 (5)

Down

1 Lazarus, for example (6)
2 Flowed back (5)
3 Raised floor with seat or throne (4)
5 'Christ was a _____ ' (*Romans 15:8*) (8)
6 'As the mouth _____ meat' (*Job 34:3*) (7)
7 The repentant one hopes for absolution (6)
8 Kosher food is this, according to Jewish law (5)
13 Old Testament book named after the son of Hachaliah (8)
15 Pagan (7)
17 Climbed (6)
18 Jacob's eighth son (5)
19 Store room such as those in 1 Chronicles 27 (6)
22 'Who shall _____ him to see?' (*Ecclesiastes 3:22*) (5)
23 Genesis 29 describes her as 'tender eyed' (4)

No 35

Across

1 'And a _____ of lies' (*Habakkuk 2:18*) (7)
5 Saul and David did this in Israel (5)
8 Numbers 21 describes a serpent made of this (5)
9 Descriptive of a punishment such as crucifixion (7)
10 Subjugate, as the Egyptians did the Israelites (7)
11 Easter often falls in this month (5)
12 Apostle and patron saint of Scotland (6)
14 Important Old Testament prophet (6)
17 Song popularised a considerable time ago (5)
19 God spoke to Moses from such a bush (7)
22 Reason given in 2 Chronicles 11 for Rehoboam's building of cities in Judah (7)
23 'They will believe the _____ of the latter sign' (*Exodus 4:8*) (5)
24 Reside, as Jeremiah did with Gedaliah in Mizpah (*Jeremiah 40*) (5)
25 Son of Bath-sheba in 1 Kings 2 (7)

Down

1 Item of furniture in Malachi 1 (5)
2 Gathered (7)
3 Husband of the prostitute, Gomer (5)
4 Sister of Leah and wife of Jacob (6)
5 Angel mentioned in the apocryphal book of Tobit (7)
6 More tardy (5)
7 Philistine woman beloved of Samson (7)
12 'And David _____ out of his presence twice' (*1 Samuel 18:11*) (7)
13 'He became the author of _____ salvation' (*Hebrews 5:9*) (7)
15 Indian religion related to Buddhism (7)
16 Convents ruled by an abbot (6)
18 English author of 'Hymn to the pillory' (5)
20 Fellow competitor (5)
21 'They shall thoroughly _____ ' (*Jeremiah 6:9*) (5)

No 36

Across

7 'His _____ goeth forth' *(Psalm 146:4)* (6)
8 She replaced Vashti as queen consort to 9 Down (6)
10 Rebekah's nurse in Genesis 35 (7)
11 Garment such as those made by Adam and Eve in Genesis 3 (5)
12 Atmosphere (4)
13 Traditional accompaniment to sackcloth (5)
17 Slumber, as Jacob did at Bethel (5)
18 Ananias, for example *(Acts 5)* (4)
22 'And being in an _____ he prayed' *(Luke 22:44)* (5)
23 'To the _____ god' *(Acts 17:23)* (7)
24 Book of the Apocrypha (6)
25 A Hebrew name for God (6)

Down

1 Shortest book of the Bible (7)
2 'All my _____ are as a shadow' *(Job 17:7)* (7)
3 Mark 4 describes how Jesus calmed this (5)
4 In Genesis 2, Adam and Eve were not (7)
5 Constituent of Jesus' crown at the crucifixion (5)
6 What the millstones do in Isaiah 47 (5)
9 King of Persia who married 8 Across (9)
14 'Therefore whosoever _____ Cain' *(Genesis 4:15)* (7)
15 Paul wrote him two epistles (7)
16 Mother's mother (7)
19 Muslim who has made the pilgrimage to Mecca (5)
20 House of Parliament in which sit Church of England bishops (5)
21 Abimelech's was broken in Judges 9 (5)

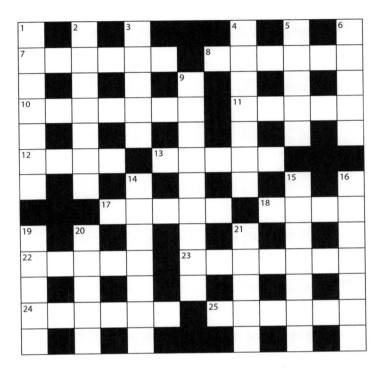

No 37

Across

1   Old Testament book and prophet (8)
7   Mountain on which Moses received the Ten Commandments (5)
8   Whitsuntide (9)
9   He chose the well-watered plain in Genesis 13 (3)
10 Old Testament prophet and herdman from Tekoa (4)
11 'And _____ to themselves instruments' (Amos 6:5) (6)
13 Proclaimer mentioned in Daniel 3 (6)
14 Animal's coat mentioned in Deuteronomy 18 (6)
17 One of two books of the Bible named after women (6)
18 Alternative name for Jerusalem (4)
20 A son of Noah (3)
22 Paul wrote them an epistle (9)
23 'The _____s, and the garlick' (Numbers 11:5) (5)
24 Water shortages, such as God called for in Haggai 1 (8)

Down

1   Town where Jonah took ship (5)
2   Spite (7)
3   Inheritors of the earth, according to the Sermon on the Mount (4)
4   'She is come aforehand to _____ my body' (Mark 14:8) (6)
5   Rested on bended knee, as in prayer (5)
6   One of an ancient people from Syria and Asia Minor (7)
7   Church spire (7)
12 Make smooth (7)
13 'A fire shall come forth out of _____' (Jeremiah 48:45) (7)
15 Tombstone inscription (7)
16 Restrain with a rope (6)
17 The modern way to contact someone (1-4)
19 'Where the birds make their _____' (Psalm 104:17) (5)
21 Hairy man, according to Genesis 27 (4)

No 38

Across

1 He was buried in Hebron in 2 Samuel 3 (5)
4 Former Wimbledon tennis champion (6)
9 Angel (7)
10 Father of Rachel and Leah (5)
11 Lot's wife was turned to this material (4)
12 Long-suffering, like Job (7)
13 Encountered (3)
14 Type of chapel dedicated to the Virgin Mary (4)
16 Fifth book of the New Testament (4)
18 Father of Joshua (3)
20 Son of David, born in Jerusalem, in 1 Samuel 5 (7)
21 'And it _____ worms, and stank' (Exodus 16:20) (4)
24 Follower of the philosopher Zeno (5)
25 Final book of the Old Testament (7)
26 'And for him that is _____ ' (Ezekiel 45:20) (6)
27 'With the blood that is in the _____ ' (Exodus 12:22) (5)

Down

1 Majestic (6)
2 David married his widow in 1 Samuel 25 (5)
3 'The _____ and the hail and the thunders' (Exodus 9:34) (4)
5 One of the recipients of an epistle from Paul (8)
6 'Elias was a man _____ to like passions as we are' (James 5:17) (7)
7 Set on fire (6)
8 Slumbered, like Adam in Genesis 2 (5)
13 Fabulous (8)
15 Father of Barak in Judges 4 (7)
17 Reason for the presence of Mary and Joseph in Bethlehem (6)
18 She asked to be called Mara in Ruth 1 (5)
19 Name taken by several popes (6)
22 'The _____ in the wilderness' (Psalm 78:15) (5)
23 Cudgel (4)

No 39

Across

1 Hebrew dialect spoken in Jesus' time (7)
8 Canaanite commander killed by Jael in Judges 4 (6)
9 Resilient (7)
11 'They also took _____ , and came to Capernaum' (John 6:24) (8)
12 Beneath (5)
14 Heavenly body followed by the magi (4)
15 More characteristic of the season of 10 Down (8)
17 Lawfulness (8)
18 African cleric, winner of Nobel Peace Prize (4)
20 'And he made ten _____ of brass' (1 Kings 7:27) (5)
21 The Jewish sabbath (8)
23 David was this son of Jesse (7)
24 'Is it not of the ____ __ hosts...?' (Habakkuk 2:13) (4,2)
25 Show dissent (7)

Down

2 Become less severe (6)
3 'And if I be a _____ ' (Malachi 1:6) (6)
4 Flower (4)
5 Marine gastropods (7)
6 Book of the Pentateuch (9)
7 'When sailing was now _____ ' (Acts 27:9) (9)
10 Christian festival (9)
12 In vain (9)
13 Rachel and Leah were those of Laban (9)
16 A clear call, as of a trumpet (7)
18 Currency unit used in biblical times (6)
19 Tithes (6)
22 'It is a ____ of rest unto the land' (Leviticus 25:5) (4)

No 40

Across

5 Great suffering, such as that of Christ on the cross (5)
8 Old Testament book (8)
9 Incline (5)
10 High priest who condemned Jesus to death (8)
11 'Consider the lilies of the _____ ' (*Matthew 6:28*) (5)
14 Bishopric (3)
16 Body of water crossed during the exodus (3,3)
17 'And there be in it a _____ thin hair' (*Leviticus 13:30*) (6)
18 Elijah asked to do this in 1 Kings 19 (3)
20 Long narrow sea inlet (5)
24 'Awake, _____ and harp' (*Psalm 57:8*) (8)
25 Range (5)
26 Whipped, as was Jesus before the crucifixion (8)
27 Problems (5)

Down

1 'I have gathered my myrrh with my _____ '
   (*Song of Solomon 5:1*) (5)
2 Bird often seen on Christmas cards (5)
3 Entice, as the devil did Jesus in the wilderness (5)
4 One dedicated, but not professed to a religious life (6)
6 Thomas could not be so described (8)
7 Former French emperor (8)
12 Youngest son of Jacob (8)
13 Unjustly seizing (8)
14 Unhappy, like the baker and butler in Genesis 40 (3)
15 Organ of sight (3)
19 Creature featuring in three of the plagues of Egypt (6)
21 'Of wheaten _____ shalt thou make them' (*Exodus 29:2*) (5)
22 Find out the heaviness of an object (5)
23 Peter healed Aeneas here in Acts 9 (5)

No 41

Across

1 'But Saul _____ to make David fall' (*1 Samuel 18:25*) (7)
5 Set pieces of work, as mentioned in Exodus 5 (5)
8 Swelling (5)
9 Breeding place of certain birds (7)
10 Thursday ten days before Whit Sunday (9)
12 'The great ___ of their right foot' (*Exodus 29:20*) (3)
13 For example, Solomon and David (6)
14 Money changers in the temple may have used this (6)
17 Proverbially patient Old Testament character (3)
18 The patron saint of the Czech Republic (9)
20 Mental pictures (7)
21 Suspension of hostilities (5)
23 Build—for example, Jacob's altar in Genesis 33 (5)
24 Old Testament prophet and book (7)

Down

1 Shin bone (5)
2 Fluid used for anointing (3)
3 For example, Ruth (7)
4 'Let us ____ __ into this city' (*Judges 19:11*) (4,2)
5 Type of hedge mentioned in Micah 7 (5)
6 Descriptive of the apostle Thomas (9)
7 Bashfulness (7)
11 'Ye shall _____ it in the seventh month' (*Leviticus 23:41*) (9)
13 Make merry, as did Hiram in 1 Kings 5 (7)
15 '_____ upon these slain' (*Ezekiel 37:9*) (7)
16 For example, pepsin (6)
18 Grain mentioned in Joel 2 (5)
19 Magical incantation (5)
22 Father of Bezaleel in Exodus 31 (3)

No 42

Across

1 Priest who signed the covenant in Nehemiah 10 (6)
4 Jezebel had him falsely accused of blasphemy (6)
7 Book of the Pentateuch (9)
9 The very first murder victim (4)
10 'Another angel ascending from the ____ ' *(Revelation 7:2)* (4)
11 One who breaks the eighth commandment (5)
13 Least wet (6)
14 Meal prepared by a certain king in Matthew 22 (6)
15 Tables used for Mass or Eucharist (6)
17 Knocked gently (6)
19 Fibre used for making rope (5)
20 First wife of Jacob (4)
22 Precious stone mentioned in Lamentations 4 (4)
23 He was seen by Jesus under a fig tree in John 1 (9)
24 Dove (6)
25 Classification according to grade (6)

Down

1 Fearful, like Cornelius in Acts 10 (6)
2 She killed Sisera in Judges 4 (4)
3 That of Goliath was six cubits and a span (6)
4 Fastened, like Jesus to the cross (6)
5 Colour of the robe of the ephod in Exodus 28 (4)
6 For example, Nimrod (6)
7 'Shall punish _____ the piercing serpent' *(Isaiah 27:1)* (9)
8 He was shipwrecked on Malta (5,4)
11 Old rulers of Russia (5)
12 Last (5)
15 Sisera was, when killed by 2 Down (6)
16 Aerated water-bottle (6)
17 Profession of Simon in Acts 10 (6)
18 Removing moisture (6)

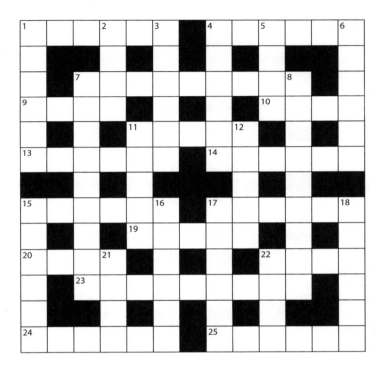

Down (continued)

21 Unclean animal according to Leviticus 11 (4)

22 What one should do on the sabbath (4)

No 43

Across

1 'But ye have borne the tabernacle of your _____ '
   (*Amos 5:26*) (6)
4 'And _____ to lift up my face' (*Ezra 9:6*) (5)
8 Indian percussion instrument (5)
9 Skies (7)
10 Meteorological noise mentioned in Exodus 9 (7)
11 Border in which was Etham in Exodus 13 (4)
12 Neither Jews nor Muslims may eat its flesh (3)
14 For example, Patmos in Revelation 1 (4)
15 So be it (4)
18 Relationship of Methuselah to Enoch (3)
21 'And now abideth faith, _____ , charity' (*1 Corinthians 13:13*) (4)
23 He fell down through a lattice in 2 Kings 1 (7)
25 A son of David, born in Jerusalem (*2 Samuel 5:15*) (7)
26 Images of gods (5)
27 Weird (5)
28 Animal's coat mentioned in Judges 6 (6)

Down

1 Undergo change (6)
2 'And all thy _____ ' (*Deuteronomy 28:33*) (7)
3 Location of Ur, original home of Abraham (8)
4 Wild animal mentioned in Hosea 13 (4)
5 Turn upside down (2-3)
6 Hurry, as Abraham did in Genesis 18 (6)
7 Like the arrows in Isaiah 5 (5)
13 A teacher of Saul (8)
16 A part of a serial (7)
17 Food substance referred to in 1 Samuel 17 (6)
19 He died before the Lord in Numbers 3 (5)
20 'I may present you as a _____ virgin' (*2 Corinthians 11:2*) (6)
22 Deputy of an abbot (5)
24 'A man plucked off his _____ ' (*Ruth 4:7*) (4)

No 44

Across

1 'Let the foundations thereof be _____ laid' (*Ezra 6:3*) (8)
7 Apostle also called Simon (5)
8 Festival of the purification of the Virgin Mary (9)
9 Land to which Cain fled after killing Abel (3)
10 Vessel from Adramyttium in Acts 27 (4)
11 Ship mentioned in Isaiah 33 (6)
13 Mendicant, such as Lazarus (6)
14 'The brother shall _____ the brother' (*Mark 13:12*) (6)
17 Book containing complete year's service for Mass (6)
18 God of the Canaanites (4)
20 Second person pronoun (3)
22 Feast of St Martin (9)
23 'And into thine _____ ' (*Exodus 8:3*) (5)
24 Legendary vanished land in the Atlantic (8)

Down

1 Subdivisions of religions (5)
2 'As a roaring lion, and a _____ bear' (*Proverbs 28:15*) (7)
3 River in which the infant Moses was found (4)
4 Old feast day, celebrated on 1 August (6)
5 'I will take the _____ heart' (*Ezekiel 11:19*) (5)
6 Child of precocious genius (7)
7 A book of psalms (7)
12 Pays for a captive's freedom (7)
13 One of its kings was Nebuchadnezzar (7)
15 Permit entrance again (7)
16 Musical instrument mentioned in Isaiah 5 (6)
17 Equine beasts, 245 of which are mentioned in Ezra 2 (5)
19 Fails to keep (5)
21 Servant of Saul in 2 Samuel 9 (4)

No 45

Across

1 Discourse on a biblical text (6)
4 Son of Jephunneh, in Numbers 13 (5)
8 Bird sent from the ark by Noah (5)
9 Egyptian ruler at the time of the exodus (7)
10 Son of King David of Israel (7)
11 Found in the church tower? (4)
12 'How is the gold become ___ !' (Lamentations 4:1) (3)
14 Chief god of Norse mythology (4)
15 'And again he denied with an ____ ' (Matthew 26:72) (4)
18 Number of camels taken by the servant in Genesis 24 (3)
21 Facial features mentioned in Amos 9 (4)
23 Belly (7)
25 Tableland (7)
26 Quotes (5)
27 'That there is one _____ unto all' (Ecclesiastes 9:3) (5)
28 Nationality of Colonel Gaddafi (6)

Down

1 Most painful (6)
2 Abused, like Jesus in Matthew 27 (7)
3 'Made the _____ of the spices' (1 Chronicles 9:30) (8)
4 Home of the eagle in Job 39 (4)
5 Permission, as Jesus gave the devils in Mark 5 (5)
6 'And now, _____ , the king walketh' (1 Samuel 12:2) (6)
7 Pay out (5)
13 He was due to be hanged in Esther 5 (8)
16 His mother was Eunice (7)
17 A place of worship (6)
19 Old Testament book and prophet (5)
20 Complete agreement (6)
22 Escape (5)
24 Jesus washed those of his disciples after the last supper (4)

No 46

Across

1 Take part in religious service (7)
5 Unclean animal according to Deuteronomy 14 (5)
8 Saul consulted a medium here (5)
9 'To morrow am I _____ unto her also' (*Esther 5:12*) (7)
10 Book of the Old Testament (9)
12 Mother of King Hezekiah (*2 Kings 18:2*) (3)
13 'An _____ of great authority' (*Acts 8:27*) (6)
14 Deliver a sermon (6)
17 Colour of certain horses in Zechariah 6 (3)
18 Concerning certain of Christ's followers (9)
20 Screen behind 21 Across (7)
21 A thespian (5)
23 Fertile spot in the desert (5)
24 'I will also gather all _____ ' (*Joel 3:2*) (7)

Down

1 'Or the _____ broken at the cistern' (*Ecclesiastes 12:6*) (5)
2 Symbol of authority carried by Aaron (3)
3 Upholder of a heresy (7)
4 Title sometimes applied to Christ or Satan (6)
5 'And in dens and _____ of the earth' (*Hebrews 11:38*) (5)
6 Disciple found by Philip in John 1 (9)
7 Jewish language not heard in Jesus' time (7)
11 Plantations such as that planted by Noah in Genesis 9 (9)
13 Prohibition or ban (7)
15 Withdraw (7)
16 Male godchild (6)
18 South American mountain range (5)
19 King of Persia mentioned in 2 Chronicles 36 (5)
22 Number of goats Aaron is commanded to take in Leviticus 16 (3)

No 47

Across

1   One of the gifts of the magi (4)
5   'To _____ up the vision' (*Daniel 9:24*) (4)
7   He hid 100 prophets from Queen Jezebel (*1 Kings 18:4*) (7)
8   King of Judah 729–686BC (8)
10 For example, Adrian or Leo (4)
12 Hairless, like every head in Jeremiah 48 (4)
14 Of the dwelling place of God (8)
16 They believe there is no God (8)
17 Descriptive of the earth before God first spoke (4)
18 His patron saint is Andrew (4)
19 'I have _____ the world' (*John 16:33*) (8)
22 Keep oneself in check (7)
23 Not kosher (4)
24 Facial feature mentioned in 2 Kings 19 (4)

Down

1   Home town of Goliath (4)
2   Bird released from the ark by Noah (4)
3   Districts assigned to a priest by the church (8)
4   Jonah was swallowed by one (4)
5   Original occupation of King David (8)
6   'Let us not _____ in word' (*1 John 3:18*) (4)
9   Flexible (7)
11 Traveller to a holy place (7)
13 Substance used for colouring cloth, and so on (8)
15 Replied, as did God to Moses in Exodus 19 (8)
18 'The priests shall cast _____ upon them' (*Ezekiel 43:24*) (4)
19 Possessive pronoun (4)
20 Cereal crop mentioned in Hosea 2 (4)
21 ' _____ homo' (4)

No 48

Across

1 Part of Esau's body grasped by Jacob at birth (4)
4 'And one ___ ___ of the first year' (*Leviticus 14:10*) (3,4)
8 Privation (8)
9 Bird of prey mentioned in Psalm 102 (3)
11 Book of the Old Testament which does not mention God (6)
13 A son of Levi in Genesis 46 (6)
14 Entrap (5)
15 Herodias' daughter asked for that of John the Baptist (4)
17 A great-grandfather of King David (4)
18 Contravene the eighth commandment (5)
20 Those worn by penitents are of hair (6)
21 Did Jonah's fish suffer from this? (6)
24 ' ___ my people go' (*Exodus 5:1*) (3)
25 Animal providing material for the king's throne in 1 Kings 10 (8)
26 Occupation of Amos (7)
27 'The ____ of his face shone' (*Exodus 34:30*) (4)

Down

2 Praise (5)
3 'Joshua _____ that night among the people' (*Joshua 8:9*) (6)
4 Reflected sound (4)
5 'To _____ them in the siege' (*Deuteronomy 20:19*) (6)
6 Alligator pear (7)
7 Babylonian king who saw the writing on the wall (10)
10 He died at the age of 969 (10)
12 Hires out (5)
13 Muslim scriptures (5)
16 Airman (7)
18 'Like a _____ of brimstone' (*Isaiah 30:33*) (6)
19 Scourges (6)
22 Peninsula crossed by Moses during the exodus (5)
23 One of the foodstuffs brought by Barzillai in 2 Samuel 17 (4)

No 49

Across

1   Corrosive fluids (5)
4   'The _____ of his fire shall not shine' (Job 18:5) (5)
10 Sleep, like the shepherds in Nahum 3 (7)
11 Sick man healed by Jesus in Matthew 8 (5)
12 'Will by no means _____ the guilty' (Exodus 34:7) (5)
13 Delighted, as was Haman in Esther 5 (7)
15 Recess at the end of a church (4)
17 He was angry with Job (5)
19 Made enquiries (5)
22 Vessel for baptismal water (4)
25 Emergency airborne operation (7)
27 Religious ceremonies (5)
29 Sound made by 21 Down (5)
30 Elevate to the peerage (7)
31 With which the wine was mingled in Mark 15 (5)
32 Job escaped with the skin of his (5)

Down

2   Vessel containing water in 1 Kings 19 (5)
3   Wife of Lapidoth in Judges 4 (7)
5   'Let them give us _____ to eat' (Daniel 1:12) (5)
6   A ready reply (7)
7   Intimidate by psychological means (5)
8   For example, tear or rain (5)
9   A group of lions (5)
14 'His flesh shall wax _____ ' (Isaiah 17:4) (4)
16 Swell up (4)
18 Forbidden by the eighth commandment (7)
20 Like the fire offered by Nadab and Abihu in Leviticus 10 (7)
21 Animals separated by Jacob in Genesis 30 (5)
23 'To speak with _____ tongues' (Acts 2:4) (5)
24 Remains of Sodom and Gomorrah, according to 2 Peter 2 (5)

Down (continued)

26 Bury (5)
28 Book of the Apocrypha (5)

No 50

Across

5 Fruit tree mentioned in Joel 1 (5)
8 Old American term for Whitsuntide (8)
9 Bird once popular as a Christmas dinner (5)
10 Short prayers (8)
11 'He will _____ thine iniquity' (*Lamentations 4:22*) (5)
14 Ask for alms, like Lazarus (3)
16 Interjection expressing merriment (3-3)
17 He prophesied famine in Acts 11 (6)
18 Cheated (*slang*) (3)
20 Throw out (5)
24 Heaven (8)
25 'As the colour of _____ ' (*Ezekiel 1:4*) (5)
26 Miniature instrument used by a campanologist (8)
27 'They hiss and _____ the teeth' (*Lamentations 2:16*) (5)

Down

1 Small particle (5)
2 Uzziel was this relation of Aaron (*Leviticus 10:4*) (5)
3 Eighth son of Jacob (5)
4 'But we were _____ among you' (*1 Thessalonians 2:7*) (6)
6 Like the son in the parable? (8)
7 Very sweet (8)
12 Twelfth son of Jacob (8)
13 Birds mentioned in Matthew 23 (8)
14 'My ___ shall comfort me' (*Job 7:13*) (3)
15 Seventh son of Jacob (3)
19 Prophet, the son of Amoz (6)
21 Title of various leaders in Sunni Islam (5)
22 Proverbially, more than Solomon? (5)
23 'Upon thy _____ shalt thou go' (*Genesis 3:14*) (5)

No 51

Across

1 They were used to bind Samson fast in Judges 16 (5)
4 'Earth was of one language, and of one ____ ' *(Genesis 11:1)* (6)
9 Exclamation of praise to God (7)
10 Tempest, such as that in Mark 4 (5)
11 Dull pain (4)
12 Of a wife (7)
13 ' ___ Maria' (3)
14 In 1 Samuel 2, that of Hannah was exalted (4)
16 Consumes (4)
18 Feature touched in Luke 22 (3)
20 Well-liked (7)
21 Item of clothing mentioned in Joshua 5 (4)
24 Type of poetry (5)
25 God is often described as such (7)
26 One of the Proverbs? (6)
27 'Let him be your ____ ' *(Isaiah 8:13)* (5)

Down

1 Warm up again (6)
2 Archaic term for Easter (5)
3 As sung by Solomon? (4)
5 Annual Jewish feast (8)
6 Conceited, boastful person (7)
7 'But giveth grace unto the ____ ' *(James 4:6)* (6)
8 The physicians in Job 13 had none (5)
13 Characteristic of the Church of England (8)
15 Golden embroidery on an ecclesiastical vestment (7)
17 Upsets (6)
18 Sinned (5)
19 Sounded like the church bells (6)
22 Door pivot mentioned in Proverbs 26 (5)
23 Manna is said to be like that of coriander, in Exodus 16 (4)

107

No 52

Across

1 Colour of one of the horses in Revelation 6 (5)
7 Most pious (8)
8 'And the _____ of thine ointments' (*Song of Solomon 4:10*) (5)
10 The song of the Virgin Mary (10)
12 The birth of Christ (8)
14 Powder found in the bathroom (4)
16 'Shall be _____ in pieces' (*Jeremiah 5:6*) (4)
17 Unmarried woman (8)
20 One without faith (10)
23 Personal memorial of a saint (5)
24 'For _____ ye were not able to bear it' (*1 Corinthians 3:2*) (8)
25 Condiment mentioned in Exodus 35 (5)

Down

1 Og was its king, according to Numbers 32 (6)
2 What the sea became after Jonah was cast into it (4)
3 One of the Gospels (4)
4 'They come up by the _____ of Ziz' (*2 Chronicles 20:16*) (5)
5 Traders mentioned in Ezekiel 27 (9)
6 Unmoving (6)
9 Immature insect (5)
11 Quality or property (9)
13 Samson dwelt in this part of the rock Etam (*Judges 15:8*) (3)
15 'With idols _____ every green tree' (*Isaiah 57:5*) (5)
16 Educated, like the children of Israel in Deuteronomy 31 (6)
18 Save, as David did his two wives in 1 Samuel 30 (6)
19 One of the plagues of Egypt (5)
21 Abbreviation for an Old Testament book (4)
22 'And to _____ his harvest' (*1 Samuel 8:12*) (4)

No 53

Across

1 Enters in a list (US) (7)
5 Description of Moses in Numbers 12 (4)
7 'That we may _____ our hearts' (Psalm 90:12) (5)
8 Sister of Moses and Aaron (6)
10 Animal used as a sin offering in Leviticus 9 (4)
11 'As it _____ the gospel of Christ' (Philippians 1:27) (8)
13 Father of Noah (6)
14 Design marked on the skin (6)
17 Member of Jewish priestly sect at the time of Christ (8)
19 Cleanse, like Pharaoh's daughter did in Exodus 2 (4)
21 For example, David v. Goliath (6)
22 Dwelling place of the Nethinims, in Nehemiah 3 (5)
23 'A wild ass ____ to the wilderness' (Jeremiah 2:24) (4)
24 Comes back (7)

Down

1 Matthew, Mark, Luke or John (10)
2 Valley in which the Philistines spread themselves in 2 Samuel 5 (7)
3 Produces eggs (4)
4 Child reared by Eli the priest (6)
5 Herb (8)
6 Rub out (5)
9 Addressee of Acts and Luke's Gospel (10)
12 Cleaned by hard rubbing (8)
15 'A _____ of babes' (Romans 2:20) (7)
16 Document written in the Syrian tongue in Ezra 4 (6)
18 Scum from melting metal, as in Proverbs 25 (5)
20 Noah's ark was a large one (4)

No 54

Across

1   'And her belly shall _____ ' (Numbers 5:27) (5)
4   'Except the Lord of _____ ' (Romans 9:29) (7)
8   The papal see was moved here in the 14th century (7)
9   A son of Aaron and Elisheba (Exodus 6:23) (5)
10 Royal Society for the Prevention of Accidents (abb.) (5)
11 'And chief _____ of Galilee' (Mark 6:21) (7)
13 Home city of Goliath (4)
15 Tree mentioned in Job 40 (6)
17 During which Moses led the Israelites (6)
20 The apostle Paul was taken to this city (4)
22 Days regarded as the sabbath by Christians (7)
24 Fifth son of Benjamin (1 Chronicles 8:2) (5)
26 'The _____ and flags shall wither' (Isaiah 19:6) (5)
27 Temporary cessation (7)
28 Full or brilliant covering or array (7)
29 Piquant, like Lot's wife? (5)

Down

1   Bird mentioned in Psalm 102 (7)
2   Ways out (5)
3   When events described in the Bible took place (4,3)
4   Nightfall (6)
5   'And he shook off the _____ ' (Acts 28:5) (5)
6   Left out, as the scribes and Pharisees did with weightier matters
    of the law in Matthew 23 (7)
7   'About the space of three _____ after' (Acts 5:7) (5)
12 A son of Noah (4)
14 Askew (4)
16 Lamp mentioned in John 18 (7)
18 Abnormal dryness of the skin (7)
19 State in which the Israelites existed in Egypt (7)
21 Bird of prey mentioned in Leviticus 11 (old spelling) (6)

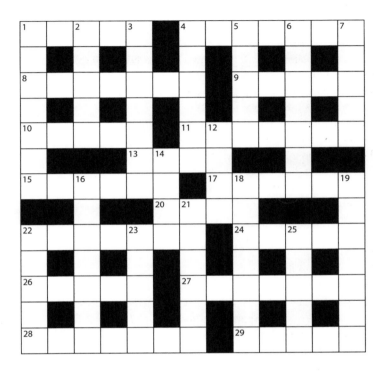

Down (continued)

22 Pilgrim's pouch (5)
23 Phrygian slave known for his fables (5)
25 Small bottle used mainly for medicine (5)

No 55

Across

1   Rings up (5)
7   'Thou shalt not _____ thyself' (*Matthew 5:33*) (8)
8   Used up (5)
10 Day commemorating Christ's crucifixion (4,6)
12 Buildings used for worship (8)
14 Feminine forename (4)
16 Gospel writer (4)
17 Areas under a bishop's jurisdiction (8)
20 One attending a religious service (10)
23 Christ walked upon it (5)
24 Miriam's feelings towards Moses? (8)
25 'And he took a _____ ' (*Mark 9:36*) (5)

Down

1   Relating to the cosmos (6)
2   'Which love to go in ____ clothing' (*Mark 12:38*) (4)
3   Material of which the ark was made in Deuteronomy 10 (4)
4   'Nor to _____ authority over the man' (*1 Timothy 2:12*) (5)
5   State of being prepared (9)
6   Entreated in the course of worship (6)
9   Implement to which the governors of Judah are likened in Zechariah 12 (5)
11 The sacrament of the Lord's Supper (9)
13 Temple priest at Shiloh in 1 Samuel (3)
15 Threaded fastener (5)
16 Description of the fables in Titus 1 (6)
18 Treated mercifully (6)
19 Number of sons fathered by Noah (5)
21 The Sunday before Easter (4)
22 'Be not ____ with thy mouth' (*Ecclesiastes 5:2*) (4)

No 56

Across

1 'Servants came to _____ our lord' (1 Kings 1:47) (5)
4 Member of the vegetable kingdom (5)
10 Captain of Saul's army in 1 Samuel 14 (5)
11 Division of Old or New Testament book (7)
12 State or time after death (8)
13 Heavenly body which does not shine in Job 25 (4)
15 Number of years lived by Enos before fatherhood, in Genesis 5 (6)
17 Money paid to kidnapper (6)
19 'Fire and hail; _____ and vapour' (Psalm 148:8) (4)
20 'And the _____ of thy molten images' (Isaiah 30:22) (8)
23 Completely or partially hide (7)
24 Insect featuring in one of the plagues of Egypt (5)
25 Employing (5)
26 He made a sound with cymbals in 1 Chronicles 16 (5)

Down

2 Weapon mentioned in Jeremiah 50 (5)
3 Samson lost his when his head was shaved (8)
5 The dove in Genesis 8 had one in her mouth (4)
6 'He shall eat up the _____ ' (Numbers 24:8) (7)
7 The Lord's Prayer (11)
8 Urgently pressing (5)
9 Relationship of Lois to Timothy, recipient of two of Paul's epistles (11)
14 Certain stories told by Christ (8)
16 Pasta ribbons (7)
18 Colour of the rods of poplar taken by Jacob in Genesis 30 (5)
21 Furnish (5)
22 Goliath's height exceeded six cubits by one of these (4)

No 57

Across

1 Musical instrument (5)
7 Clergy home (8)
8 Leader of the tribe of Zebulun, in Numbers 1 (5)
10 King who had a feast in Daniel 5 (10)
12 Companion of Meshach and Abednego (8)
14 'Them that dwell in houses of ____ ' (Job 4:19) (4)
16 Creature appearing in the chief baker's dream in Genesis 40 (4)
17 Festival celebrated on 6 January (8)
20 Scene of the final battle between good and evil (10)
23 Husband of Abigail in 1 Samuel 25 (5)
24 Spice mentioned in Exodus 30 (8)
25 Apostle to the Gauls and patron saint of France (5)

Down

1 Produces offspring (6)
2 He blew a trumpet in 2 Samuel 2 (4)
3 'Let me, I pray thee, ____ my father' (1 Kings 19:20) (4)
4 He was hanged in Esther 7 (5)
5 He brought supplies to King David in 2 Samuel 17 (9)
6 Treacherously give information about, as Judas did to Jesus (6)
9 2 Down took Amasa by this in 2 Samuel 20 (5)
11 Bread or wine taken in celebration of the Lord's Supper (9)
13 'Having a golden ___ in her hand' (Revelation 17:4) (3)
15 Utensil whose handle sometimes bears a figure of an apostle (5)
16 Offshoot from the main trunk (6)
18 Gives up (6)
19 Wife of David in 2 Samuel 3 (5)
21 'And stood in the ____ of their tents' (Numbers 16:27) (4)
22 Main part of a church (4)

No 58

Across

1 Instrument played by David in 1 Samuel 16 (4)
4 Nebuchadnezzar was one of its kings (7)
8 Descriptive of King Herod's home? (8)
9 Location of the Royal Botanic Gardens (3)
11 Telephoned (6)
13 Lamech was this relation of Noah (6)
14 Abimelech had one in Genesis 20 (5)
15 The image in Daniel 2 had legs of this metal (4)
17 Passport endorsement (4)
18 'I will make _____ mountains' (Isaiah 42:15) (5)
20 Abounded (6)
21 Psalm 10 asks God not to forget them (6)
24 Herb mentioned in Luke 11 (3)
25 Vestry (8)
26 'The master and the _____ ' (Malachi 2:12) (7)
27 Level (4)

Down

2 Be of service to (5)
3 Communed with God (6)
4 Inflamed swelling, like those suffered by Job (4)
5 Owner of a speaking ass (6)
6 Hindu goddess of beauty, wealth and pleasure (7)
7 For example, Sophie Raworth (10)
10 Sacred writings (10)
12 'Let not thy _____ make me afraid' (Job 13:21) (5)
13 It is said to move mountains (5)
16 'This is a nation that _____ not' (Jeremiah 7:28) (7)
18 Small carnivore mentioned in Leviticus 11 (6)
19 Mother of Timothy in 2 Timothy 1 (6)
22 'Nor _____ his flesh' (Leviticus 17:16) (5)
23 Mark left by a wound (4)

No 59

Across

1 Monster mentioned in Job 40 (8)
7 Islamic holy war (5)
8 Wife of Uriah the Hittite in 2 Samuel 11 (9)
9 Male cat (3)
10 'There hath not been _____ the like' (Joel 2:2) (4)
11 Father of Moses' wife Zipporah (6)
13 Bovines created by God in Genesis 1 (6)
14 Acts 9 mentions one called Straight (6)
17 Waxen cylinder blessed on 2 February (6)
18 Roman emperor renowned for his harsh treatment of the early Christians (4)
20 Fluid used for anointing (3)
22 For example, Zerah in 2 Chronicles 14 (9)
23 Thoroughly unpleasant (5)
24 'And embrace the bosom of a _____ ' (Proverbs 5:20) (8)

Down

1 Old and New Testaments together (5)
2 'The forefront of the _____ battle' (2 Samuel 11:15) (7)
3 Part of a ship mentioned in Isaiah 33 (4)
4 Martin Luther nailed 95 of these to the church door in Wittenberg (6)
5 Snapshot (5)
6 'Made their hearts as an _____ stone' (Zechariah 7:12) (7)
7 One of eight survivors of the flood (7)
12 Cloth used for washing (7)
13 He did not recognise Jesus in Luke 24 (7)
15 Time of day for evensong (7)
16 Out of date (3,3)
17 Rock face such as that of Ziz in 2 Chronicles 20 (5)
19 'And his _____ hath not kept him in' (Exodus 21:36) (5)
21 Garment possibly worn by Pontius Pilate (4)

No 60

Across

1 Descriptive of the place the swine ran down in Matthew 8 (5)
4 Like sails pressed backwards on the mast (5)
10 'To cause my heart to _____ ' (Ecclesiastes 2:20) (7)
11 Amos 6 mentions beds of this material (5)
12 Beasts of the forest do this in Psalm 104 (5)
13 This is boiled to make porridge (7)
15 'Unto Aholah and unto Aholibah, the ____ women' (Ezekiel 23:44) (4)
17 'Let it be done with _____ ' (Ezra 6:12) (5)
19 A place of sacrifice (5)
22 Contest for recreation (4)
25 Had sleeping visions, like Jacob in Genesis 28 (7)
27 Stage performer (5)
29 A son of Abraham (5)
30 Home of the recipients of an epistle from Paul (7)
31 'I am _____ and Omega' (Revelation 1:8) (5)
32 First plant created by God in Genesis 1 (5)

Down

2 'Is there any _____ in the white of an egg?' (Job 6:6) (5)
3 'For an _____ of suffering affliction' (James 5:10) (7)
5 Constructed, like Uzziah's towers in 2 Chronicles 26 (5)
6 Disease of the intestine (7)
7 Decree (5)
8 Missile mentioned in Lamentations 3 (5)
9 A recurring series of changes (5)
14 God made one of this man's ribs into a woman (4)
16 'Make fifty loops on the ____ ' (Exodus 26:10) (4)
18 'Fifteen cubits upward did the waters _____ ' (Genesis 7:20) (7)
20 2 Kings 1 mentions a girdle of this material (7)
21 Let in (5)
23 Genesis 49 compares Dan to this snake (5)

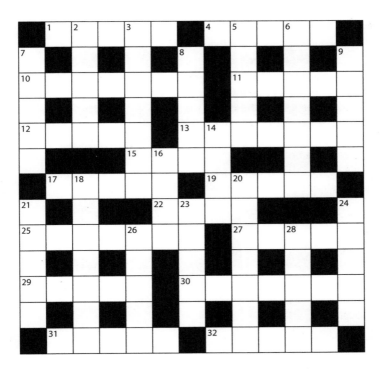

Down (continued)

24 On which Jesus was crucified (5)

26 Old Testament book (5)

28 Pieces of work assigned to the Israelites in Exodus 5 (5)

No 61

Across

1   'For the _____ is full' (*Joel 3:13*) (5)
4   Underground chapel (5)
10 Day upon which God rested after the creation (7)
11 A grandson of Esau in Genesis 36 (5)
12 Carnivore related to the civet (5)
13 Teachers of the Law of Moses (7)
15 'Then Absalom called _____ him' (*2 Samuel 15:2*) (4)
17 Italian cathedral (5)
19 A king of Midian killed in Numbers 31 (5)
22 Relationship of Miriam to Nadab, son of Aaron (4)
25 'There is none _____ among men' (*Micah 7:2*) (7)
27 Daniel prospered during his reign in Daniel 6 (5)
29 Theatrical show (5)
30 Major Old Testament prophet (7)
31 'And Moses _____ shall come near' (*Exodus 24:2*) (5)
32 Putting to some purpose (5)

Down

2   Black bird mentioned in Song of Solomon 5 (5)
3   A sacred place (7)
5   Barber's tool mentioned in Ezekiel 5 (5)
6   Story told by Jesus to illustrate a point (7)
7   Customary practice (5)
8   Large box for money in 2 Chronicles 24 (5)
9   Abyss (5)
14 Cereal crop wasted in Joel 1 (4)
16 He became drunk in Genesis 9 (4)
18 Disentangle (7)
20 Engravers (7)
21 David set Benaiah over his in 2 Samuel 23 (5)
23 'Nor my tongue _____ deceit' (*Job 27:4*) (5)
24 Devotional song (5)

Down (continued)

26 Gather overlooked 14 Down, like Ruth (5)

28 Rule, like David or Solomon (5)

No 62

Across

4 The children of men speak with such a heart in Psalm 12 (6)
5 Inflamed swelling on 6 Down (4)
7 Body of water mentioned in Numbers 20 (7)
10 Joshua gave him Hebron in Joshua 14 (5)
11 'The acts of Zimri, and his _____ ' (1 Kings 16:20) (7)
12 Christian name of whodunnit author Miss Marsh (5)
14 'Teaching them to _____ all things' (Matthew 28:20) (7)
15 Italian religious painter (1406–69) (5)
16 'To _____ concerning Judah' (alternative spelling) (Ezra 7:14) (7)
20 Weapon used by David against Goliath (5)
21 Liquid skincare preparations (7)
22 Jacob pitched his in the mount in Genesis 31 (4)
23 Territory ruled by Og, in Numbers, Deuteronomy and so on (6)

Down

1 Unit of length frequently mentioned in the Bible (5)
2 Seaweeds (5)
3 Unusual, like the apparel in Zephaniah 1 (7)
4 That of Jehoiachin was continual in Jeremiah 52 (4)
6 Facial feature mentioned in Jeremiah 9 (6)
8 Offering illegal inducements (7)
9 Loathsome, like the unclean birds in Revelation 18 (7)
10 Change from one faith to another (7)
13 Grain mentioned in Ezekiel 4 (6)
14 'There can be no _____ ' (Job 12:14) (7)
17 Very small amounts (5)
18 Number of years Israel was judged by Abdon in Judges 12 (5)
19 'And ____ they tell him of her' (Mark 1:30) (4)

No 63

Across

1 Son of Abraham and Sarah (5)
4 That of a pilgrim is a scallop shell (5)
10 'Go and _____ the sackcloth' (*Isaiah 20:2*) (5)
11 Shale-oil (*American*) (4-3)
12 Sabbath day for the Jewish faith (8)
13 Old Testament book named after a herdman of Tekoa (4)
15 Paul asks his readers to salute this man in Romans 16 (6)
17 Mother of Samuel (6)
19 Third son of Adam and Eve (4)
20 He succeeded Solomon in 1 Kings 12 (8)
23 He laid hands on Saul in Acts 9 (7)
24 Norwegian dramatist (5)
25 Aromatic gum mentioned in Psalm 45 (5)
26 'I heard the second _____ say' (*Revelation 6:3*) (5)

Down

2 Pig's nose, as mentioned in Proverbs 11 (5)
3 Sinful (8)
5 King of Israel 874–853BC (4)
6 'And the king said, He is a _____ _____ ' (*2 Samuel 18:27*) (4,3)
7 2 November (3,5,3)
8 Fragment (5)
9 Speaking impiously of God (11)
14 Enrol in the list of saints (8)
16 Home town of Lazarus in John 11 (7)
18 For example, Epiphany (5)
21 Fertile spot in the desert (5)
22 'For he is a _____ , and the father of it' (*John 8:44*) (4)

No 64

Across

1 Weapons like that mentioned in Jeremiah 50 (6)
4 Son of Manasseh in Genesis 50 (6)
7 Thursday ten days before Whit Sunday (9)
9 Mother of Jesus (4)
10 Saul's body was fastened to this in 1 Samuel 31 (4)
11 Shoot, like those pruned in Isaiah 18 (5)
14 King of Heshbon in Deuteronomy 2 (5)
15 Full of water (5)
16 Head of an abbey (5)
17 Son of Ner in 1 Chronicles 26 (5)
18 'The elder unto the _____ lady' (2 John 1) (5)
20 'My people have committed two _____' (Jeremiah 2:13) (5)
23 Plant like those about Jonah's head in Jonah 2 (4)
25 Perform again (4)
26 Third book of the Pentateuch (9)
27 Inclines (6)
28 Break in church unity (6)

Down

1 Feast day celebrated on 1 August (6)
2 Snug (4)
3 Be unconscious, like Adam in Genesis 2 (5)
4 African tribe of Kenya and Tanzania (5)
5 'The cock shall not _____' (John 13:38) (4)
6 City in the land of Hamath in Jeremiah 39 (6)
7 Angel of the highest order (9)
8 Inhabitants of Jesus' home town (9)
11 Bird trap mentioned in Ecclesiastes 9 (5)
12 Jesus is addressed thus in John 1 (5)
13 Entrances like that used by Jehu in 2 Kings 9 (5)
17 At all times (6)
19 Religion widespread in China (6)

Down (continued)

21 'And the hoods, and the _____ ' (*Isaiah 3:23*) (5)

22 'His strength is in his _____ ' (*Job 40:16*) (5)

24 Descriptive of Abram's 3 Down in Genesis 15 (4)

25 Old Testament book named after a woman (4)

No 65

Across

5   Elevated platform (5)
8   Book of the Old Testament (8)
9   Brother of Moses (5)
10 Sanhedrin president condemning Jesus to death (8)
11 'As free, and not _____ your liberty' (1 Peter 2:16) (5)
14 Lodging house which was fully booked in Luke 2 (3)
16 Language of Christian descendants of ancient Egyptians (6)
17 'Instructing those that _____ themselves' (2 Timothy 2:25) (6)
18 'For Christ is the ___ of the law' (Romans 10:4) (3)
20 Inhabitant of a certain Middle Eastern town (5)
24 Venomous arthropod mentioned in Luke 11 (8)
25 Piece of leftover food (5)
26 Home of Cornelius in Acts 10 (8)
27 Gales blowing in Matthew 7 (5)

Down

1   Condiment brought by the rulers in Exodus 35 (5)
2   A book of the Apocrypha (5)
3   Jumps, like the rams upon the cattle in Genesis 31 (5)
4   'They also may _____ mercy' (Romans 11:31) (6)
6   Part of church at right angles to the nave (8)
7   'Fear the Lord and his _____ ' (Hosea 3:5) (8)
12 Adoptive father of Esther (8)
13 'Set up the _____ towards Zion' (Jeremiah 4:6) (8)
14 Reason for the brooks being blackish in Job 6 (3)
15 Head movement signifying approval (3)
19 Sweet liquid produced by plants (6)
21 Refuse taken from silver in Proverbs 25 (5)
22 Daily journal (5)
23 Work dough, like the women in Jeremiah 7 (5)

No 66

Across

1 Decoration of a printed character (5)
4 Military expedition to recover the Holy Land (7)
8 Angel of the bottomless pit in Revelation 9 (7)
9 Ornament by inserting pieces of contrasting material (5)
10 Dissent (5)
11 Person having no belief in God (7)
13 Girl's name (4)
15 Missile used to kill Goliath? (6)
17 Food trough in which the infant Jesus was laid (6)
20 Abbreviated form of Christmas (4)
22 Headgear worn by Roman Catholic priest (7)
24 King of Tyre in 2 Samuel 5 (5)
26 Colour of horses in the second chariot in Zechariah 6 (5)
27 'Lest thou also be _____ ' (*Galatians 6:1*) (7)
28 Book of the Apocrypha (7)
29 Die in water, like Pharaoh's captains (*Exodus 15:4*) (5)

Down

1 'There shall _____ __ yet three kings' (*Daniel 11:2*) (5,2)
2 Jehoshaphat's is described as quiet in 2 Chronicles 20 (5)
3 Type of government in which several states combine (7)
4 The promised land (6)
5 Soldier in David's army, and husband of Bathsheba (5)
6 Joining (7)
7 Moses led the children of Israel away from here (5)
12 A son of Ishmael in Genesis 25 (4)
14 'For Mordecai the Jew was ____ ' (*Esther 10:3*) (4)
16 Interments such as that of Stephen in Acts 8 (7)
18 Abashed, like the Philistines' daughters in Ezekiel 16 (7)
19 Ninth month of the Muslim calendar (7)
21 Sister of Mary in Luke 10 (6)
22 Infants mentioned in 1 Peter 2 (5)

Down (continued)

23 'Who hath _____ this counsel…?' (Isaiah 23:8) (5)

25 Proportion (5)

No 67

Across

1 The first Pope (5,5)
8 'The time of the _____ oblation' (Daniel 9:21) (7)
9 Plant of the heath genus (5)
10 Length of Og's bedstead in cubits in Deuteronomy 3 (4)
11 Beverage drunk by Belshazzar in Daniel 5 (4)
12 Father of Hophni and Phinehas in 1 Samuel 1 (3)
14 Cellars found beneath churches (6)
15 Flirtatious young woman (6)
18 Second person created by God (3)
20 Alternative name of Esau (4)
21 Great man in Joshua 14 (4)
23 A son of David born in Jerusalem in 2 Samuel 5 (5)
24 Philistine giant slain by David (7)
25 Notified, as did Balaam (Numbers 24:14) (10)

Down

1 Rigorously (7)
2 Coloured part of the eye (4)
3 Modern name of the river Hiddekel in Daniel 10 (6)
4 Critical interpretation of a biblical text (8)
5 'The captive _____ hasteneth' (Isaiah 51:14) (5)
6 King of Assyria who dwelt at Nineveh in 2 Kings 19 (11)
7 Biography of 1 Across or 13 Down? (11)
13 Patron saint of England (2,6)
16 Floral wreath like those mentioned in Acts 14 (7)
17 Purchased, as Joseph did fine linen in Mark 15 (6)
19 Priestly garment made by Gideon in Judges 8 (5)
22 'And Joshua said, _____ , O Lord God' (Joshua 7:7) (4)

No 68

Across

1 Wife of Elimelech in Ruth 1 (5)
7 Tepid (8)
8 'For the _____ is full' (Joel 3:13) (5)
10 For example, Abishag in 1 Kings 1 (10)
12 Traveller (8)
14 'Good _____ from a far country' (Proverbs 25:25) (4)
16 'For this is the whole _____ of man' (Ecclesiastes 12:13) (4)
17 Admitted to holy orders (8)
20 Act of reverence (10)
23 For example, Francis of Assisi (5)
24 Everlasting (8)
25 Yellowish colour mentioned in Ezekiel 1 (5)

Down

1 Relation of which Abdon had 30 in Judges 12 (6)
2 Celebration of Eucharist (4)
3 'I will _____ her chariots' (Nahum 2:13) (4)
4 Pieces of timber mentioned in Nehemiah 2 (5)
5 Inhabitants of northern Palestine in Luke 13 (9)
6 Red hot ashes (6)
9 Bundle of corn-stalks like those in Amos 2 (5)
11 Onlooker (9)
13 Facial feature cut off in Luke 22 (3)
15 Rings around the heads of holy persons (5)
16 'Arise, _____ much flesh' (Daniel 7:5) (6)
18 Person owing money (6)
19 'Lust of the eyes, and the _____ of life' (1 John 2:16) (5)
21 Noah was uncovered in his in Genesis 9 (4)
22 A son of Caleb in 1 Chronicles 4 (4)

No 69

Across

1 Apostle who betrayed Jesus (5)
4 Type of hedge mentioned in Micah 7 (5)
10 Dry, like Sisera in Judges 4 (7)
11 Cluster, as of hyssop in Exodus 12 (5)
12 Relating to Solomon or Herod? (5)
13 'Make for it a grate of _____ of brass' (*Exodus 27:4*) (7)
15 Licentious revel (4)
17 Dishonour, as received by Ephraim in Hosea 10 (5)
19 'In _____ place incense shall be offered' (*Malachi 1:11*) (5)
22 Recess at the east end of a church (4)
25 Line used for pulling (7)
27 Daughter of a sibling (5)
29 Bend forward, like the proud helpers in Job 9 (5)
30 In Psalm 74 they are set up for signs (7)
31 Relating to an irritating sensation (5)
32 'In everlasting chains _____ darkness' (*Jude 6*) (5)

Down

2 'Till we all come in the _____ of the faith' (*Ephesians 4:13*) (5)
3 A son of King David (7)
5 Garment worn by monks (5)
6 Bitterness (7)
7 Heavenly bodies mentioned in Daniel 12 (5)
8 'Shall we be consumed with _____ ?' (*Numbers 17:13*) (5)
9 Smother, as thorns did the seeds in Matthew 13 (5)
14 Scales fell from Saul's in Acts 9 (4)
16 Gather in, like the harvest in 1 Samuel 8 (4)
18 'Which he had _____ _____ in the rock' (*Matthew 27:60*) (4,3)
20 Meat mentioned in Genesis 25 (7)
21 Stow in hiding (5)
23 Writer of two New Testament epistles (5)
24 Division of a biblical chapter (5)

Down (continued)

26 Daughter-in-law of Naomi in Ruth 1 (5)
28 Bird of prey mentioned in Habakkuk 1 (5)

No 70

Across

6   Two days after Good Friday (6,6)
8   'And if the _____ of blood pursue' (Joshua 20:5) (7)
9   Versification (5)
10 Profit, as mentioned in James 4 (4)
12 That of God filled Bezaleel in Exodus 31 (6)
14 Recipient of an epistle of Paul (5)
15 King in Proverbs 31 (6)
16 'All they which are in _____ ' (2 Timothy 1:15) (4)
19 Sense of which Samson was deprived (5)
21 Armour bearer of Joab in 1 Chronicles 11 (7)
22 One section of the Bible (3,9)

Down

1   Doctrine of a small fraternity among the ancient Jews (8)
2   Thorny barrier mentioned in Micah 7 (5)
3   'Thou hast taken _____ ' (Ezekiel 22:12) (5)
4   Removes covering (7)
5   Chapel dedicated to the Virgin Mary (4)
6   For example, the apostle John (10)
7   The Greek 22 Across (10)
11 Fluid used to make the face shine in Psalm 104 (3)
12 'The ___ of the sons of Gershon' (Numbers 4:22) (3)
13 Strings of beads used by Roman Catholics (8)
14 Having made a will (7)
17 Strike one's teeth together, like the wicked in Psalm 112 (5)
18 Cereal crop threshed by Gideon in Judges 6 (5)
20 The whole house in 1 Kings 6 was overlaid with this (4)

No 71

Across

1 Killer of Gedaliah in 2 Kings 25 (7)
8 Chief religion of Japan (6)
9 Of a branch of the Benedictine order (7)
11 Apostle chosen to replace Judas Iscariot (8)
12 Descriptive of the fishes in Mark 8 (5)
14 ' ____ in ten days store of all sorts of wine' (Nehemiah 5:18) (4)
15 Tribe, descendants of Esau (8)
17 Difficulties which are forgotten in Isaiah 65 (8)
18 'And oil is carried ____ Egypt' (Hosea 12:1) (4)
20 Emotion experienced by Ahasuerus in Esther 1 (5)
21 Distance from tip to tip of, for example, Gabriel's wings (8)
23 Most yielding (7)
24 Rocked, as did the earth in Isaiah 24 (6)
25 Places of Christian worship (7)

Down

2 Descriptive of the harp's sound in Psalm 92 (6)
3 Mix, like glass and fire in Revelation 15 (6)
4 Fifth son of Meshelemiah in 1 Chronicles 26 (4)
5 Patterns of recurrent sound (7)
6 Descriptive of the oil made by Bezaleel in Exodus 37 (9)
7 According to Genesis 14, that of heaven and earth is God (9)
10 Festival celebrated on 2 February (9)
12 'Get you up this way _____ ' (Numbers 13:17) (9)
13 'Which also were _____ giants' (Deuteronomy 2:11) (9)
16 Ashamed (7)
18 Part of the foot (6)
19 Prickly plant (6)
22 His sons were Ham, Shem and Japheth (4)

No 72

Across

1 Number of chapters in the book of Micah (5)
4 Material of the sea in Revelation 6 (5)
10 Land attached to a parish church (5)
11 The disciples were first called Christians here (7)
12 Nationality of Hagar in Genesis 16 (8)
13 Lowest female voice in the choir (4)
15 'He covered them on the _____ ' (1 Kings 6:15) (6)
17 Primitive religion of African origin (6)
19 'Even unto Ithiel and ____ ' (Proverbs 30:1) (4)
20 King of Judah 597–586BC (8)
23 A cradle song (7)
24 On which the feeble were carried in 2 Chronicles 28 (5)
25 'That ye _____ to be quiet' (1 Thessalonians 4:11) (5)
26 Scatter (5)

Down

2 Foe like Haman in Esther 7 (5)
3 Time of day when Isaac went to meditate in Genesis 24 (8)
5 'The Jews of ____ sought to stone thee' (John 11:8) (4)
6 Plundered, like the Philistines' tents in 1 Samuel 17 (7)
7 Prominently (11)
8 The Devil (5)
9 Person supposed wise in affairs of God (literal meaning) (11)
14 Agreement such as that between God and the Israelites (8)
16 Colour of robe placed on Jesus in Matthew 27 (7)
18 Material of the eighth foundation in Revelation 21 (5)
21 'These waters _____ out toward the east' (Ezekiel 47:8) (5)
22 Body part to which a cloud is compared in 1 Kings 18 (4)

No 73

Across

1 The pastoral staff of a bishop (7)
7 These are acceptable as a burnt offering according to Leviticus 1 (5)
8 'An ____ ___ seeketh only rebellion' (*Proverbs 17:11*) (4,3)
9 A petition to God (6)
11 Grain meal taken by the woman in 1 Samuel 28 (5)
13 In addition (4)
14 Book of the Pentateuch (7)
15 Third god of the Hindu triad (4)
16 Gum carried by the Ishmeelites in Genesis 37 (5)
17 'There shall not be room _____ to receive it' (*Malachi 3:10*) (6)
21 Cords used on bows as in Psalm 11 (7)
22 Part of Jezebel's body found in 2 Kings 9 (5)
23 Composer of songs of praise (7)

Down

2 Book written by St John the Divine (10)
3 Midianite king beaten by Gideon in Judges 8 (8)
4 A son of Shem in Genesis 10 (4)
5 Number of bowls in the candlestick in Exodus 37 (4)
6 'He shall ____ with his hand' (*1 Samuel 16:16*) (4)
9 Communion plate (5)
10 Confectionery given as gifts at a Christian festival (6,4)
12 Metal worker mentioned in Isaiah 44 (5)
13 Nationality of Sargon in Isaiah 20 (8)
18 Trees like that under which Deborah was buried in Genesis 35 (4)
19 'Between us and you there is a great ____ ' (*Luke 16:26*) (4)
20 ' ____ me with flagons' (*Song of Solomon 2:5*) (4)

No 74

Across

1   Father of Rehum in Nehemiah 3 (4)
5   City from which Hiram came in 1 Kings 9 (4)
7   'Perplexed, but not in _____ ' (2 Corinthians 4:8) (7)
8   Traditional dragon slayer (2,6)
10 Burrowing animal mentioned in Leviticus 11 (4)
12 Midianite killed in Numbers 31 (4)
14 Companion of Meshach and Abednego (8)
16 Name of two kings of Israel (8)
17 Bird worshipped by the ancient Egyptians (4)
18 Abbreviation often found on a crucifix (1,1,1,1)
19 For example, David and Solomon (8)
22 'And chief _____ of Galilee' (Mark 6:21) (7)
23 Shelled fruits mentioned in Genesis 43 (4)
24 A child of Shobal in Genesis 36 (4)

Down

1   A knob or stud (4)
2   The devil is said to find work for such hands (4)
3   Type of coffee (8)
4   Piece of barley bread which tumbled in Judges 7 (4)
5   The Hindu triad (8)
6   'My couch shall ____ my complaint' (Job 7:13) (4)
9   'And put fire _____ , and put incense' (Numbers 16:7) (7)
11 Amaziah fled here in 2 Kings 14 (7)
13 Tribe delivered up by the Lord in Joshua 10 (8)
15 One of a tribe mentioned in Jeremiah 49 (8)
18 In the Eastern churches, an image representing Christ (4)
19 Insect mentioned in Job 28 (4)
20 Isaiah 35 mentions this flower (4)
21 Innermost being or nature (4)

No 75

Across

1 ' _____ them as the mire of the street' (2 *Samuel* 22:43) (5)
4 Mollusc mentioned in Psalm 58 (5)
10 Aromatic plants mentioned in Deuteronomy 11 (5)
11 Did he fall from heaven in Isaiah 14? (7)
12 Leah's fifth son (8)
13 Son of Seth, according to Luke 3 (4)
15 Doubting apostle (6)
17 Body of water parted by Moses during the exodus (3,3)
19 'Let down your _____ for a draught' (*Luke* 5:4) (4)
20 Side of the choir opposite the decani (8)
23 'Durst not shew you mine _____ ' (*Job* 32:6) (7)
24 Consumed, like the sour grape in Jeremiah 31 (5)
25 Colour of the throne in Revelation 20 (5)
26 Steal a king's throne (5)

Down

2 (Formerly) inhabitants of the Ottoman empire (5)
3 For example, David when playing the harp (8)
5 Zedekiah stiffened his in 2 Chronicles 36 (4)
6 Young people mentioned in Luke 18 (7)
7 That part of the world where Christianity is the prevalent religion (11)
8 The Muslim name for God (5)
9 Sinning (11)
14 The covering of, for example, 16 Down (8)
16 Bird mentioned in Job 39 (7)
18 For example, Andrew or Patrick (5)
21 A rotating aerofoil (5)
22 One of the 10 Across mentioned in Luke 11 (4)

No 76

Across

1 Alternative name for Abednego in Daniel 1 (7)
5 Pillar called Boaz in 1 Kings 7 (4)
7 The trunk of the human body (5)
8 'And shall _____ many people' (Isaiah 2:4) (6)
10 Exclamation apologising for a mistake (4)
11 'Yet for all this _____ not I the bread' (Nehemiah 5:18) (8)
13 Prophet and Old Testament book (6)
14 Small carnivore which is unclean according to Leviticus 11 (6)
17 Candace was queen of this area in Acts 8 (8)
19 'Burn it in the fire: it is _____ inward' (Leviticus 13:55) (4)
21 Name taken by several Popes (6)
22 Garment worn by a priest at Mass (5)
23 'Gone through the _____ unto Paphos' (Acts 13:6) (4)
24 Big cat mentioned in Ezekiel 19 (7)

Down

1 Version of the Bible also known as King James (10)
2 King mentioned in Acts 25 (7)
3 Worshipped by 9 Down (4)
4 Insect mentioned in Joshua 24 (6)
5 Workman worthy of his hire according to Luke 10 (8)
6 Muslim mendicant (5)
9 She is guilty of breaking the second commandment (10)
12 Enrol in the list of saints (8)
15 Performance of religious worship (7)
16 Sweet fruit cake traditionally eaten at Easter (6)
18 Alternative name for hell (5)
20 Ring round a holy person's head (4)

No 77

Across

1 Numbered musical composition (4)
4 One of the birds in Psalm 102 (7)
8 Joseph was a slave to this officer of Pharaoh's (8)
9 Timber of which 6 Down were constructed (3)
11 Birds that gathered together in Matthew 24 (6)
13 'I have heard thy _____ ' (Habakkuk 3:2) (6)
14 Upset, like the water in 2 Samuel 14 (5)
15 'All the beasts of the field ____ ' (Job 40:20) (4)
17 Very promptly (abb.) (1,1,1,1)
18 Fragment of food eaten by Lazarus in Luke 16 (5)
20 Mountain on which the ark landed (6)
21 Mother of Timothy, recipient of an epistle from Paul (6)
24 Son of Ikkesh the Tekoite in 2 Samuel 23 (3)
25 Jacob was this relation to Abraham (8)
26 Strip of cloth worn at the throat (7)
27 Home of the great owl in Isaiah 34 (4)

Down

2 Spike of a forked object (5)
3 Condiments given to Solomon by Sheba (2 Chronicles 9:1) (6)
4 Old hunting cry; London district (4)
5 Sudden (6)
6 Roof supports mentioned in Song of Solomon 1 (7)
7 Churchgoer (10)
10 'And in time of _____ fall away' (Luke 8:13) (10)
12 'That he may make us _____ ' (Judges 16:25) (5)
13 Moses' ark was daubed with this, according to Exodus 2 (5)
16 Language probably spoken by Jesus (7)
18 Entangled, like the ram in Genesis 22 (6)
19 That of Nineveh is the book of Nahum (1:1) (6)
22 Their worship is forbidden by the Ten Commandments (5)
23 Cook, as Lot did unleavened bread in Genesis 19 (4)

No 78

Across

1 'Much _____ is a weariness of the flesh' (*Ecclesiastes 12:12*) (5)
4 Waste matter mentioned in Proverbs 25 (5)
10 Animal dismembered by Elijah in 1 Kings 18 (7)
11 The King James version, perhaps (5)
12 Perform like Herodias' daughter in Matthew 14 (5)
13 Dried fruit mentioned in 2 Samuel 16 (7)
15 Third son of Adam and Eve (4)
17 'I have been an _____ in a strange land' (*Exodus 18:3*) (5)
19 Jacob's second son by Zilpah (*Genesis 35:26*) (5)
22 Oil was sold to pay this in 2 Kings 4 (4)
25 'The _____ seats in the synagogues' (*Luke 20:46*) (7)
27 Leaf brought back to the ark by the dove (5)
29 Deadly (5)
30 Liar and husband of Sapphira (7)
31 Songs of praise (5)
32 Colour of wool traded by Damascus in Ezekiel 27 (5)

Down

2 Claw (5)
3 Extent of a bishop's jurisdiction (7)
5 Leader of a Jewish synagogue (5)
6 Exalted (7)
7 'I must _____ at thy house' (*Luke 19:5*) (5)
8 David cut off Saul's in 1 Samuel 24 (5)
9 Easter, for example (5)
14 King of Israel and husband of Jezebel (4)
16 'The _____ of the staves were seen' (*1 Kings 8:8*) (4)
18 'And all the hills moved _____ ' (*Jeremiah 4:24*) (7)
20 1 Timothy 5 advises us to use wine for the sake of this (7)
21 Psalm 1 mentions this grain refuse (5)
23 Son of Kishi in 1 Chronicles 6 (5)
24 Stop, like the hail in Exodus 9 (5)

Down (continued)

26 King of Moab in Judges 3 (5)
28 Foolish person (5)

No 79

Across

5 Utensil made by Bezaleel in Exodus 37 (5)
8 Figure of Christ on the cross (8)
9 'Didst thou not _____ with me…?' (*Matthew 20:13*) (5)
10 Festival commemorating the visit of the magi (8)
11 Strike the teeth together, like the wicked in Psalm 112 (5)
14 The waters ran in such places in Psalm 105 (3)
16 Centre of Christianity in the Byzantine Empire (6)
17 Festival commemorating Christ's resurrection (6)
18 'Lest he ___ him fenced cities' (*2 Samuel 20:6*) (3)
20 'That had seen the _____ house' (*Ezra 3:12*) (5)
24 Son of King Saul and friend of David (8)
25 Pharaoh is compared to this sea creature in Ezekiel 32 (5)
26 Religion founded by Gautama (8)
27 Romany (5)

Down

1 Ten of these measures of vineyard yield one bath, according to Isaiah 5 (5)
2 One fiftieth of the height of Haman's gallows (*Esther 5:14*) (5)
3 Do battle, as did Sihon at Jahaz in Deuteronomy 2 (5)
4 One who commits a moral or religious offence (6)
6 Heathenism (8)
7 Exceed (8)
12 Adjective often applied to God (8)
13 For example, James and John, the sons of Zebedee (8)
14 Abner compared himself to the head of this animal in 2 Samuel 3 (3)
15 'For he was ___ in the loins of his father' (*Hebrews 7:10*) (3)
19 The going out of the Israelites from Egypt (6)
21 Moses' were heavy in Exodus 17 (5)
22 The part of a church allotted to the singers (5)
23 His kisses are deceitful, according to Proverbs 27 (5)

No 80

Across

1 Remission of sins, declared by a priest (10)
8 Gangster (7)
9 Tree that spoke in Judges 9 (5)
10 First black bishop of Johannesburg (4)
11 Type of church service (4)
12 For example, sergeant or corporal (1,1,1)
14 Serviceable (6)
15 'The lion did tear in pieces _____ for his whelps' (Nahum 2:12) (6)
18 Male cat (3)
20 Track in which stood the angel in Numbers 22 (4)
21 To cut short, as were the beards in Jeremiah 48 (4)
23 Tibet's Head Lama (5)
24 Painted halo (7)
25 Tent housing the ark of the covenant (10)

Down

1 One of Christ's twelve chosen followers (7)
2 'Ananias, with Sapphira his wife, ___ a possession' (Acts 5:1) (4)
3 Feast day celebrated on 1 August (6)
4 Number of men killed by Samson in Judges 15 (8)
5 Pungent root mentioned in Numbers 11 (5)
6 The season of Pentecost (11)
7 Fourth king of Judah (878–842BC) (11)
13 White linen vestment worn over the cassock (8)
16 'I am not worthy to stoop down and _____ ' (Mark 1:7) (7)
17 ' _____ at a gnat, and swallow a camel' (Matthew 23:24) (6)
19 Modern name of the island where the apostle Paul was shipwrecked (5)
22 Acid in the blood, crystals of which cause gout (4)

Solutions

No 1

Across

5 Hippo 8 Caiaphas 9 Often 10 Benjamin 11 Angel 14 Eli
16 Gideon 17 Nathan 18 Dan. 20 River 24 Idolatry 25 Devil
26 Redeemer 27 Itchy

Down

1 Scabs 2 Lions 3 Spear 4 Daniel 6 Infinite 7 Plebeian 12
Diligent 13 Jeremiah 14 End 15 Inn 19 Andrew 21 Bleed
22 Stamp 23 Myrrh

No 2

Across

1 Thyself 5 Amour 8 Cargo 9 Witch of 10 Teacher 11 Omega
12 Needle 14 Chosen 17 Manna 19 Leprosy 22 Ephesus
23 Endor 24 Simon 25 Agendas

Down

1 Tacit 2 Yardage 3 Enoch 4 Few are 5 Antioch 6 Ochre
7 Refrain 12 Numbers 13 Liaison 15 Scolded 16 Elisha
18 Nahum 20 Piece 21 Yarns

No 3

Across

1 Accept 4 Dream 8 Cello 9 Washpot 10 Nicaean 11 Tyre
12 Err 14 Lamb 15 Ezra 18 Sea 21 Idle 23 Crozier/Crosier
25 Lucifer 26 Ocean 27 Water 28 Smites

Down

1 Ascend 2 Cilicia 3 Proverbs 4 Dust 5 Empty 6 Mother
7 Swine 13 Rehoboam 16 Raiment 17 Willow 19 Acorn
20 Wrings 22 Licit 24 Afar

No 4

Across

1 Heal 3 Adultery 9 Syria 10 Banshee 11 Ark 13 Processed
14 Punish 16 Strand 18 Abjection 20 Sun 22 Armoire
23 Credo 25 Hosannas 26 Levi

Down

1 Hosea 2 Air 4 Debtor 5 Longest 6 Ephesians 7 Yielded
8 Harp 12 King James 14 Pharaoh 15 Section 17 Sisera
19 Neck 21 Naomi 24 Eve

No 5

Across

1 Avail 4 Spirit 9 Perjury 10 Tidal 11 Esau 12 Captain
13 Ash 14 Moab 16 Amen 18 Air 20 Abaddon 21 Shui
24 Thine 25 Ezekiel 26 Ashdod 27 Layer

Down

1 Apples 2 Aorta 3 Laud 5 Potiphar 6 Radiate 7 Talent
8 Lynch 13 Abednego 15 Obadiah 17 Martha 18 Anger
19 Pillar 22 Hairy 23 Cell

No 6

Across

1 Ararat 4 Letter 9 Apostle 10 Treat 11 East 12 Ancestor
14 Altercation 18 Epistles 20 Elam 22 Heart 23 Inmates
24 Become 25 Unused

Down

1 Amalek 2 Arousal 3 Acts 5 Entreaty 6 Theft 7 Retire
8 Sennacherib 13 Teetotum 15 Oblates 16 Rechab 17 Amused
19 Isaac 21 Omen

No 7

Across

1 Myself 4 Zigzag 7 Leviathan 9 Hoes 10 Reap 11 Bread
13 Priory 14 Rental 15 Sailor 17 Decree 19 Minor 20 Paul
22 Gnat 23 Sepulchre 24 Belial 25 Samuel

Down

1 Mishap 2 Ewes 3 Friary 4 Zethar 5 Gear 6 Gospel
7 Leviticus 8 Nectarine 11 Broom 12 Deter 15 Superb
16 Ritual 17 Dorcas 18 Entail 21 Levi 22 Grim

No 8

Across

3 Communion 8 Pain 9 Anglican 10 Cudgel 13 Yeast
14 Utilise 15 Ass 16 Hectare 17 Basil 21 Lounge
22 Covenant 23 Jehu 24 Pentecost

Down

1 Apocrypha 2 Hindrance 4 Opals 5 Maggots 6 Nail 7 Omar
11 Dissenter 12 Beelzebub 14 Use 15 Aramaic 18 Altos
19 Mote 20 Lent

No 9

Across

1 Bartimaeus 8 High Tea 9 Pride 10 Leek 11 Mary 12 Lot
14 Strong 15 Silver 18 Ira 20 Tare 21 Plan 23 Exile
24 Ephraim 25 Infallible

Down

1 Bugbear 2 Ruth 3 Isaiah 4 Asphyxia 5 Uriel 6 Philistines
7 Deuteronomy 13 Anathema 16 Vulgate 17 Ordeal 19 Alien
22 Ahab

No 10

Across

5 Isaac 8 Nehemiah 9 Brass 10 Diocesan 11 Spill 14 Sir
16 Haggai 17 Olives 18 Nod 20 Essay 24 Cherubim 25 Fruit
26 Cathedra 27 Palsy

Down

1 Anode 2 Chaos 3 Amber 4 Wahabi 6 Seraphim 7 Absolved
12 Caesarea 13 Ignatius 14 Sin 15 Rod 19 Ophrah 21 Ortho
22 Abide 23 Amman

No 11

Across

1 Gateau 4 Tragic 7 Bethlehem 9 Span 10 Mild 11 Blood
13 School 14 Regret 15 Behold 17 Statue 19 Sects 20 Robe
22 Gold 23 Adoration 24 Dogmas 25 Holier

Down

1 Guests 2 Eden 3 Uphill 4 Tremor 5 Ahem 6 Credit
7 Bathsheba 8 Migration 11 Boils 12 Debts 15 Buried
16 Debris 17 Stitch 18 Endear 21 Edom 22 Goal

No 12

Across

1 Buckle 4 Abram 8 Lilac 9 Ishmael 10 Embargo 11 When
12 Nun 14 Urim 15 Abel 18 Ash 21 Rose 23 Examine
25 Speak to 26 Enoch 27 Sidon 28 Chisel

Down

1 Belief 2 Caliber 3 Lachryma 4 Ache 5 Reach 6 Melons
7 Simon 13 Nazareth 16 Editors 17 Trusts 19 Herod
20 Bethel 22 Spend 24 Skin

No 13

Across

7 Eyelid 8 Herald 10 Diocese 11 Delve 12 Noah 13 Manna
17 Ephod 18 Herb 22 Hosea 23 Useless 24 Elands 25
Geneva

Down

1 Pending 2 Deborah 3 Wives 4 Wedding 5 Vault 6 Adder
9 Decalogue 14 Upwards 15 Zebedee 16 Abishag 19 Three
20 Islam 21 Peter

No 14

Across

1 Grape 4 Moses 10 Spill 11 Abishai 12 Leonardo 13 Gath
15 Aaron 17 Worms 21 Urge 22 Blushing 25 Goliath
26 Image 27 Acute 28 Mecca

Down

2 Rhino 3 Pillar of 5 Omit 6 Ephraim 7 Psalm 8 Lands
9 Light 14 Lot's wife 16 Angelic 18 Purge 19 Elihu 20 Egret
23 Isaac 24 Salt

No 15

Across

1 Joachim 5 Tunic 8 Dwell 9 Timothy 10 Engrave 11 Resat
12 Lord is 14 Floral 17 Rajas 19 In doubt 22 Expiate
23 Eliab 24 Yeast 25 Numbers

Down

1 Judge 2 Avenger 3 Halma 4 Mother 5 Timbrel 6 Notes
7 Crystal 12 Larceny 13 Instant 15 Reunite 16 Simeon
18 Joppa 20 Dream 21 Tubes

No 16

Across

5 Glebe 8 Homicide 9 Abner 10 Marriage 11 Stone 14 Rod
16 Priory 17 Aholah 18 Ebb 20 Snide 24 Shadrach 25 Mercy
26 Entreats 27 Strip

Down

1 Chime 2 Smart 3 Scrip 4 Adagio 6 Libation 7 Biennial
12 Transept 13 Mordecai 14 Rye 15 Dab 19 Behind 21 Adorn
22 Laban 23 Chest

No 17

Across

1 Guard 4 Lazarus 8 Dead Sea 9 Dread 10 Igloo 11 Sikhism
13 Seed 15 Rachel 17 Origin 20 Mile 22 Kingdom 24 Cream
26 Reeve 27 Glucose 28 Nettles 29 Ethos

Down

1 Godlier 2 Avail 3 Dispose 4 Liaise 5 Zadok 6 Reeking
7 Sodom 12 Idol 14 Elmo 16 Convert 18 Recluse
19 Numbers 21 Images 22 Koran 23 Dwell 25 Enoch

No 18

Across

1 Strap 8 Sapphira 9 Water 10 Together 11 Paint 12 Sea
16 Haggai 17 Deacon 18 Nod 23 Habit 24 Pharisee 25 Vigil
26 Idolater 27 Flies

Down

2 Tearaway 3 Abednego 4 Salome 5 Apses 6 Light 7 Padre
12 Sin 13 Add 14 Gamaliel 15 Homicide 19 Opened
20 Spoil 21 Carob 22 Vital

No 19

Across

1 Talmai 5 Scribe 8 Thistles 9 Yank 10 Asti 11 Nebulous
13 Jehoshaphat 15 Drawback 17 Lamb 19 Acts 20 Launders
21 Poirot 22 Scythe

Down

2 Ashes 3 Messiah 4 Inland sea 5 SOS 6 Royal 7 Banquet
12 Blackouts 13 Jericho 14 Holiday 16 Wiser 18 Myrrh
20 Lot

No 20

Across

1 Browse 4 Christ 7 Fishermen 9 Dirt 10 Dice 11 Anglo
14 Satan 15 Flood 16 Grief 17 Curse 18 Every 20 Rider
23 Roar 25 Lush 26 Languages 27 Lowest 28 Elijah

Down

1 Brides 2 Whit 3 Ethan 4 Carol 5 Reed 6 Thread 7 Fraternal
8 Nicodemus 11 Anger 12 Grind 13 Offer 17 Carmel
19 Yahweh 21 Ingot 22 Erase 24 Rake 25 Levi

No 21

Across

1 Curse 4 Abacus 9 Printer 10 Heath 11 Edom 12 Nemesis
13 Ant 14 Lamb 16 Tyre 18 Ash 20 Diamond 21 Obey
24 Abihu 25 Ezekiel 26 Dagger 27 Hiked

Down

1 Copper 2 Rhino 3 Eats 5 Behemoth 6 Coarser 7 Schism
8 Grant 13 Absolute 15 Amazing 17 Edward 18 Adder
19 Eyelid 22 Brick 23 Leah

No 22

Across

1 Rumba 4 Sailors 8 Bisects 9 Sitar 10 Cacti 11 Reeking
13 Boaz 15 Andrew 17 Rachel 20 Noah 22 Redness 24 Isaac
26 Lance 27 Riotous 28 Company 29 Meets

Down

1 Rebecca 2 Music 3 Ascribe 4 Sisera 5 Issue 6 Ostrich
7 Shrug 12 Ezra 14 Owns 16 Dedanim 18 Ahinoam
19 Locusts 21 Osprey 22 Relic 23 Enema 25 Atone

No 23

Across

1 Felony 4 Stank 8 Topaz 9 Obadiah 10 Scourge 11 Whit
12 Arc 14 Cyst 15 Ruth 18 Ham 21 Once 23 Escapee
25 Cardiac 26 Frogs 27 Sling 28 Exodus

Down

1 Fetish 2 Leprosy 3 Nazareth 4 Seal 5 Amish 6 Kohath
7 Hosea 13 Crucifix 16 Typhoid 17 Dorcas 19 Mecca
20 Census 22 Corgi 24 Ring

No 24

Across

1 Loll 5 Corn 7 Abigail 8 Epiphany 10 Ruby 12 Halo
14 Issachar 16 Baptised 17 Lent 18 Thai 19 Fluoride
22 Harvest 23 Font 24 Even

Down

1 Lice 2 Lamp 3 Litanies 4 Lady 5 Clerical 6 Navy 9 Pharaoh
11 Brained 13 Outright 15 Sadducee 18 Turf 19 Fire 20 Rite
21 Eden

No 25

Across

1 Aside 4 Enoch 10 Overall 11 Of use 12 Copts 13 Shiites
15 Easy 17 Judas 19 Merry 22 King 25 Encrust 27 Grace
29 Bleed 30 Laughed 31 Entry 32 Usury

Down

2 Sleep 3 Dead Sea 5 Naomi 6 Cluster 7 Pouch 8 Glass
9 Verse 14 Hymn 16 Asks 18 Unclean 20 Eggcups 21 Herbs
23 Italy 24 Weeds 26 Under 28 Abhor

No 26

Across

7 Anoint 8 Orally 10 Apostle 11 Moses 12 Iron 13 White
17 Sheep 18 Dove 22 Above 23 Endless 24 Esther 25 Bright

Down

1 Samaria 2 Solomon 3 Unity 4 Primate 5 Bless 6 Gypsy
9 Bethlehem 14 Thieves 15 Foreign 16 Density 19 Raven
20 Forth 21 Adore

No 27

Across

1 Whitsun 5 Meek 7 Lupin 8 Bethel 10 Evil 11 Stoicism
13 Nathan 14 Jasper 17 Servants 19 Arid 21 Ticket 22 Linen
23 Seek 24 Example

Down

1 Wilderness 2 Imprint 3 Song 4 Naboth 5 Mythical 6 Elemi
9 Imprudence 12 Habakkuk 15 Parsnip 16 Statue 18 Raise
20 Flea

No 28

Across

1 Admit 4 Philip 9 Harpist 10 Nicer 11 Oche 12 Numbers
13 Ark 14 Shem 16 Iona 18 Nod 20 Restore 21 Root
24 Rabbi 25 Aramaic 26 Tandem 27 Seeds

Down

1 Ashdod 2 Myrrh 3 Toil 5 Handmaid 6 Lectern 7 Perish
8 Stank 13 Ammonite 15 Heshbon 17 Ararat 18 Nebat
19 Stocks 22 Orate 23 Mass

No 29

Across

1 Hair 3 Caesarea 9 Style 10 Tabitha 11 Asa 13 Overacted 14
Rhombi 16 Thrown 18 Bathsheba 20 Son 22 Ill will
23 Owing 25 Suckling 26 Mete

Down

1 Hosea 2 Ivy 4 Anthem 5 Sabbath 6 Rotations 7 Abandon
8 Nero 12 Apostolic 14 Rabbits 15 Bestial 17 Berlin 19 Amos
21 Nagge 24 Ice

No 30

Across

1 Pulpit 4 Relic 8 Ripon 9 Unclean 10 Idiotic 11 Asia
12 Ham 14 Ogen 15 Oath 18 God 21 Sown 23 In Doubt
25 Harvest 26 Comet 27 Royal 28 Simmer

Down

1 Persis 2 Lapwing 3 Igniting 4 Rock 5 Leeks 6 Canaan
7 Bunch 13 Mordecai 16 Thummim 17 Esther 19 Dieth
20 Stater 22 Worry 24 Well

No 31

Across

1 Black 4 Tombs 10 Ikebana 11 Hence 12 Hanoi 13 Abishag
15 Cana 17 Babel 19 Asher 22 Salt 25 Kingdom 27 Eight
29 Eagle 30 Supreme 31 Stalk 32 Penny

Down

2 Lie in 3 Chalice 5 Ophni 6 Banshee 7 Right 8 Laban
9 Reign 14 Baal 16 Also 18 At night 20 Steeple 21 Skies
23 Amasa 24 Utter 26 Dwell 28 Glean

No 32

Across

5 Spade 8 Parables 9 Hurry 10 Chaldees 11 Beans 14 See
16 Pilate 17 Locust 18 Try 20 Birds 24 Abednego 25 Storm
26 Jebusite 27 Bring

Down

1 Speck 2 Dream 3 Abode 4 Revere 6 Prudence 7 Darkness
12 Minister 13 Mandarin 14 Set 15 Ely 19 Rubies 21 Odour
22 Peril 23 Power

No 33

Across

1 Black 4 Flock 10 Capella 11 Tooth 12 Abram 13 Nephews
15 Boaz 17 Paean 19 Roman 22 Year 25 Betwixt 27 Peter
29 Cameo 30 Ananias 31 Stays 32 Psalm

Down

2 Leper 3 Columba 5 Let up 6 Cholera 7 Scrap 8 Manna
9 Chasm 14 Ezra 16 Onyx 18 Attempt 20 Orphans 21 Aback
23 Etham 24 Cross 26 Ivory 28 Trial

No 34

Across

1 Bread 4 Smiths 9 Gabriel 10 Nisan 11 Adds 12 Austere
13 Nun 14 Shoe 16 Echo 18 Air 20 Chapels 21 Oboe
24 Lahmi 25 Ezekiel 26 Dinghy 27 Hagar

Down

1 Beggar 2 Ebbed 3 Dais 5 Minister 6 Tasteth 7 Sinner
8 Clean 13 Nehemiah 15 Heathen 17 Scaled 18 Asher
19 Cellar 22 Bring 23 Leah

No 35

Across

1 Teacher 5 Ruled 8 Brass 9 Capital 10 Enslave 11 April
12 Andrew 14 Elijah 17 Oldie 19 Burning 22 Defence
23 Voice 24 Dwell 25 Solomon

Down

1 Table 2 Amassed 3 Hosea 4 Rachel 5 Raphael 6 Later
7 Delilah 12 Avoided 13 Eternal 15 Jainism 16 Abbeys
18 Defoe 20 Rival 21 Glean

No 36

Across

7 Breath 8 Esther 10 Deborah 11 Apron 12 Aura 13 Ashes
17 Sleep 18 Liar 22 Agony 23 Unknown 24 Judith
25 Elohim

Down

1 Obadiah 2 Members 3 Storm 4 Ashamed 5 Thorn 6 Grind
9 Ahasuerus 14 Slayeth 15 Timothy 16 Grandma
19 Hadji/Hajji 20 Lords 21 Skull

No 37

Across

1 Jeremiah 7 Sinai 8 Pentecost 9 Lot 10 Amos 11 Invent
13 Herald 14 Fleece 17 Esther 18 Zion 20 Ham 22 Ephesians
23 Onion 24 Droughts

Down

1 Joppa 2 Rancour 3 Meek 4 Anoint 5 Knelt 6 Hittite
7 Steeple 12 Flatten 13 Heshbon 15 Epitaph 16 Tether
17 E-mail 19 Nests 21 Esau

No 38

Across

1 Abner 4 Agassi 9 Gabriel 10 Laban 11 Salt 12 Patient
13 Met 14 Lady 16 Acts 18 Nun 20 Elishua 21 Bred
24 Stoic 25 Malachi 26 Simple 27 Basin

Down

1 August 2 Nabal 3 Rain 5 Galatian 6 Subject 7 Ignite
8 Slept 13 Mythical 15 Abinoam 17 Census 18 Naomi
19 Adrian 22 Rocks 23 Club

No 39

Across

1 Aramaic 8 Sisera 9 Elastic 11 Shipping 12 Under 14 Star
15 Wintrier 17 Legality 18 Tutu 20 Bases 21 Saturday
23 Seventh 24 Lord of 25 Protest

Down

2 Relent 3 Master 4 Iris 5 Limpets 6 Leviticus 7 Dangerous
10 Christmas 12 Uselessly 13 Daughters 16 Clarion 18 Talent
19 Tenths 22 Year

No 40

Across

5 Agony 8 Proverbs 9 Slope 10 Caiaphas 11 Field 14 See
16 Red Sea 17 Yellow 18 Die 20 Fjord 24 Psaltery 25 Ambit
26 Scourged 27 Snags

Down

1 Spice 2 Robin 3 Tempt 4 Oblate 6 Gullible 7 Napoleon
12 Benjamin 13 Usurping 14 Sad 15 Eye 19 Insect 21 Flour
22 Weigh 23 Lydda

No 41

Across

1 Thought 5 Tasks 8 Bulge 9 Rookery 10 Ascension 12 Toe
13 Rulers 14 Abacus 17 Job 18 Wenceslas 20 Imagery
21 Truce 23 Erect 24 Ezekiel

Down

1 Tibia 2 Oil 3 Gleaner 4 Turn in 5 Thorn 6 Sceptical
7 Shyness 11 Celebrate 13 Rejoice 15 Breathe 16 Enzyme
18 Wheat 19 Spell 22 Uri

No 42

Across

1 Abijah 4 Naboth 7 Leviticus 9 Abel 10 East 11 Thief
13 Driest 14 Dinner 15 Altars 17 Tapped 19 Sisal 20 Leah
22 Ruby 23 Nathanael 24 Pigeon 25 Rating

Down

1 Afraid 2 Jael 3 Height 4 Nailed 5 Blue 6 Hunter
7 Leviathan 8 Saint Paul 11 Tsars 12 Final 15 Asleep
16 Siphon 17 Tanner 18 Drying 21 Hare 22 Rest

No 43

Across

1 Moloch 4 Blush 8 Tabla 9 Heavens 10 Thunder 11 Edge
12 Pig 14 Isle 15 Amen 18 Son 21 Hope 23 Ahaziah
25 Elishua 26 Idols 27 Eerie 28 Fleece

Down

1 Mutate 2 Labours 3 Chaldees 4 Bear 5 Up-end 6 Hasten
7 Sharp 13 Gamaliel 16 Episode 17 Cheese 19 Nadab
20 Chaste 22 Prior 24 Shoe

No 44

Across

1 Strongly 7 Peter 8 Candlemas 9 Nod 10 Ship 11 Galley
13 Beggar 14 Betray 17 Missal 18 Baal 20 You 22 Martinmas
23 Ovens 24 Atlantis

Down

1 Sects 2 Ranging 3 Nile 4 Lammas 5 Stony 6 Prodigy
7 Psalter 12 Ransoms 13 Babylon 15 Readmit 16 Tabret
17 Mules 19 Loses 21 Ziba

No 45

Across

1 Sermon 4 Caleb 8 Raven 9 Pharaoh 10 Solomon 11 Bell
12 Dim 14 Odin 15 Oath 18 Ten 21 Eyes 23 Abdomen
25 Plateau 26 Cites 27 Event 28 Libyan

Down

1 Sorest 2 Reviled 3 Ointment 4 Crag 5 Leave 6 Behold
7 Spend 13 Mordecai 16 Timothy 17 Temple 19 Nahum
20 Unison 22 Evade 24 Feet

No 46

Across
1 Worship 5 Coney 8 Endor 9 Invited 10 Leviticus 12 Abi
13 Eunuch 14 Preach 17 Bay 18 Apostolic 20 Reredos
21 Actor 23 Oasis 24 Nations

Down
1 Wheel 2 Rod 3 Heretic 4 Prince 5 Caves 6 Nathanael
7 Yiddish 11 Vineyards 13 Embargo 15 Retract 16 Godson
18 Andes 19 Cyrus 22 Two

No 47

Across
1 Gold 5 Seal 7 Obadiah 8 Hezekiah 10 Pope 12 Bald
14 Heavenly 16 Atheists 17 Dark 18 Scot 19 Overcome
22 Forbear 23 Tref 24 Nose

Down
1 Gath 2 Dove 3 Parishes 4 Fish 5 Shepherd 6 Love 9 Elastic
11 Pilgrim 13 Dyestuff 15 Answered 18 Salt 19 Ours 20 Corn
21 *Ecce*

No 48

Across
1 Heel 4 Ewe lamb 8 Hardship 9 Owl 11 Esther 13 Kohath
14 Decoy 15 Head 17 Boaz 18 Steal 20 Shirts 21 Nausea
24 Let 25 Elephant 26 Herdman 27 Skin

Down
2 Exalt 3 Lodged 4 Echo 5 Employ 6 Avocado 7 Belshazzar
10 Methuselah 12 Rents 13 Koran 16 Aviator 18 Stream
19 Lashes 22 Sinai 23 Bean

No 49

Across

1 Acids 4 Spark 10 Slumber 11 Leper 12 Clear 13 Pleased
15 Apse 17 Elihu 19 Asked 22 Font 25 Airlift 27 Rites
29 Bleat 30 Ennoble 31 Myrrh 32 Teeth

Down

2 Cruse 3 Deborah 5 Pulse 6 Riposte 7 Psych 8 Drops
9 Pride 14 Lean 16 Puff 18 Larceny 20 Strange 21 Lambs
23 Other 24 Ashes 26 Inter 28 Tobit

No 50

Across

5 Apple 8 Pinkster 9 Goose 10 Collects 11 Visit 14 Beg
16 Tee-hee 17 Agabus 18 Did 20 Eject 24 Paradise 25 Amber
26 Handbell 27 Gnash

Down

1 Speck 2 Uncle 3 Asher 4 Gentle 6 Prodigal 7 Luscious
12 Benjamin 13 Chickens 14 Bed 15 Gad 19 Isaiah 21 Mahdi
22 Wiser 23 Belly

No 51

Across

1 Ropes 4 Speech 9 Hosanna 10 Storm 11 Ache 12 Uxorial
13 *Ave* 14 Horn 16 Eats 18 Ear 20 Popular 21 Shoe 24 Lyric
25 Eternal 26 Saying 27 Dread

Down

1 Reheat 2 Pasch 3 Song 5 Passover 6 Egotist 7 Humble
8 Value 13 Anglican 15 Orphrey 17 Spills 18 Erred 19 Pealed
22 Hinge 23 Seed

No 52

Across

1 Black 7 Godliest 8 Smell 10 Magnificat 12 Nativity 14 Talc
16 Torn 17 Spinster 20 Unbeliever 23 Relic 24 Hitherto
25 Spice

Down

1 Bashan 2 Calm 3 John 4 Cliff 5 Merchants 6 Static 9 Larva
11 Attribute 13 Top 15 Under 16 Taught 18 Rescue 19 Flies
21 Esth 22 Reap

No 53

Across

1 Enrolls 5 Meek 7 Apply 8 Miriam 10 Goat 11 Becometh
13 Lamech 14 Tattoo 17 Sadducee 19 Wash 21 Combat
22 Ophel 23 Used 24 Returns

Down

1 Evangelist 2 Rephaim 3 Lays 4 Samuel 5 Marjoram 6 Erase
9 Theophilus 12 Scrubbed 15 Teacher 16 Letter 18 Dross 20
Boat

No 54

Across

1 Swell 4 Sabaoth 8 Avignon 9 Abihu 10 RoSPA 11 Estates
13 Gath 15 Willow 17 Exodus 20 Rome 22 Sundays
24 Rapha 26 Reeds 27 Respite 28 Panoply 29 Salty

Down

1 Sparrow 2 Exits 3 Long ago 4 Sunset 5 Beast 6 Omitted
7 Hours 12 Shem 14 Awry 16 Lantern 18 Xerosis 19 Slavery
21 Ospray 22 Scrip 23 Aesop 25 Phial

No 55

Across

1 Calls 7 Forswear 8 Spent 10 Good Friday 12 Churches
14 Enid 16 John 17 Dioceses 20 Worshipper 23 Water
24 Sisterly 25 Child

Down

1 Cosmic 2 Long 3 Wood 4 Usurp 5 Readiness 6 Prayed
9 Torch 11 Eucharist 13 Eli 15 Screw 16 Jewish 18 Spared
19 Three 21 Palm 22 Rash

No 56

Across

1 Bless 4 Plant 10 Abner 11 Chapter 12 Eternity 13 Moon
15 Ninety 17 Ransom 19 Snow 20 Ornament 23 Eclipse
24 Louse 25 Using 26 Asaph

Down

2 Lance 3 Strength 5 Leaf 6 Nations 7 Paternoster 8 Acute
9 Grandmother 14 Parables 16 Noodles 18 Green 21 Equip
22 Span

No 57

Across

1 Banjo 7 Vicarage 8 Eliab 10 Belshazzar 12 Shadrach 14 Clay
16 Bird 17 Epiphany 20 Armageddon 23 Nabal 24 Cinnamon
25 Denis/Denys

Down

1 Breeds 2 Joab 3 Kiss 4 Haman 5 Barzillai 6 Betray 9 Beard
11 Sacrament 13 Cup 15 Spoon 16 Branch 18 Yields
19 Eglah 21 Door 22 Nave

No 58

Across

1 Harp 4 Babylon 8 Palatial 9 Kew 11 Called 13 Father
14 Dream 15 Iron 17 Visa 18 Waste 20 Teemed 21 Humble
24 Rue 25 Sacristy 26 Scholar 27 Even

Down

2 Avail 3 Prayed 4 Boil 5 Balaam 6 Lakshmi 7 Newsreader
10 Scriptures 12 Dread 13 Faith 16 Obeyeth 18 Weasel
19 Eunice 22 Bathe 23 Scar

No 59

Across

1 Behemoth 7 Jihad/Jehad 8 Bathsheba 9 Tom 10 Ever
11 Jethro 13 Cattle 14 Street 17 Candle 18 Nero 20 Oil
22 Ethiopian 23 Awful 24 Stranger

Down

1 Bible 2 Hottest 3 Mast 4 Theses 5 Photo 6 Adamant
7 Japheth 12 Flannel 13 Cleopas 15 Evening 16 Old hat
17 Cliff 19 Owner 21 Toga

No 60

Across

1 Steep 4 Aback 10 Despair 11 Ivory 12 Creep 13 Oatmeal
15 Lewd 17 Speed 19 Altar 22 Game 25 Dreamed 27 Actor
29 Isaac 30 Ephesus 31 Alpha 32 Grass

Down

2 Taste 3 Example 5 Built 6 Cholera 7 Edict 8 Arrow 9 Cycle
14 Adam 16 Edge 18 Prevail 20 Leather 21 Admit 23 Adder
24 Cross 26 Micah 28 Tasks

No 61

Across

1 Press 4 Crypt 10 Seventh 11 Zerah 12 Genet 13 Scribes
15 Unto 17 Duomo 19 Rekem 22 Aunt 25 Upright 27 Cyrus
29 Revue 30 Ezekiel 31 Alone 32 Using

Down

2 Raven 3 Sanctum 5 Razor 6 Parable 7 Usage 8 Chest
9 Chasm 14 Corn 16 Noah 18 Unravel 20 Etchers 21 Guard
23 Utter 24 Psalm 26 Glean 28 Reign

No 62

Across

4 Double 5 Stye 7 Meribah 10 Caleb 11 Treason 12 Ngaio
14 Observe 15 Lippi 16 Enquire 20 Sling 21 Lotions 22 Tent
23 Bashan

Down

1 Cubit 2 Algae 3 Strange 4 Diet 6 Eyelid 8 Bribing 9 Hateful
10 Convert 13 Millet 14 Opening 17 Iotas 18 Eight 19 Anon

No 63

Across

1 Isaac 4 Badge 10 Loose 11 Coal-oil 12 Saturday 13 Amos
15 Urbane 17 Hannah 19 Seth 20 Rehoboam 23 Ananias
24 Ibsen 25 Myrrh 26 Beast

Down

2 Snout 3 Aberrant 5 Ahab 6 Good man 7 All Souls Day
8 Scrap 9 Blaspheming 14 Canonise 16 Bethany 18 Feast
21 Oasis 22 Liar

No 64

Across

1 Lances 4 Machir 7 Ascension 9 Mary 10 Wall 11 Sprig
14 Sihon 15 Awash 16 Abbot 17 Abner 18 Elect 20 Evils
23 Weed 25 Redo 26 Leviticus 27 Slopes 28 Schism

Down

1 Lammas 2 Cosy 3 Sleep 4 Masai 5 Crow 6 Riblah
7 Archangel 8 Nazarenes 11 Snare 12 Rabbi 13 Gates
17 Always 19 Taoism 21 Veils 22 Loins 24 Deep 25 Ruth

No 65

Across

5 Stage 8 Proverbs 9 Aaron 10 Caiaphas 11 Using 14 Inn
16 Coptic 17 Oppose 18 End 20 Adeni 24 Scorpion
25 Scrap 26 Caesarea 27 Winds

Down

1 Spice 2 Tobit 3 Leaps 4 Obtain 6 Transept 7 Goodness
12 Mordecai 13 Standard 14 Ice 15 Nod 19 Nectar 21 Dross
22 Diary 23 Knead

No 66

Across

1 Serif 4 Crusade 8 Abaddon 9 Inlay 10 Demur 11 Atheist
13 Anne 15 Pebble 17 Manger 20 Xmas 22 Biretta 24 Hiram
26 Black 27 Tempted 28 Susanna 29 Drown

Down

1 Stand up 2 Realm 3 Federal 4 Canaan 5 Uriah 6 Allying
7 Egypt 12 Tema 14 Next 16 Burials 18 Ashamed
19 Ramadan 21 Martha 22 Babes 23 Taken 25 Ratio

No 67

Across
1 Saint Peter 8 Evening 9 Erica 10 Nine 11 Wine 12 Eli
14 Crypts 15 Fizgig 18 Eve 20 Edom 21 Arba 23 Ibhar
24 Goliath 25 Advertised

Down
1 Sternly 2 Iris 3 Tigris 4 Exegesis 5 Exile 6 Sennacherib
7 Hagiography 13 St George 16 Garland 17 Bought 19 Ephod
22 Alas

No 68

Across
1 Naomi 7 Lukewarm 8 Press 10 Shunammite 12 Wayfarer
14 News 16 Duty 17 Ordained 20 Veneration 23 Saint
24 Unending 25 Amber

Down
1 Nephew 2 Mass 3 Burn 4 Beams 5 Galileans 6 Embers
9 Sheaf 11 Bystander 13 Ear 15 Halos 16 Devour 18 Debtor
19 Pride 21 Tent 22 Naam

No 69

Across
1 Judas 4 Thorn 10 Thirsty 11 Bunch 12 Royal 13 Network
15 Orgy 17 Shame 19 Every 22 Apse 25 Towrope 27 Niece
29 Stoop 30 Ensigns 31 Itchy 32 Under

Down
2 Unity 3 Absalom 5 Habit 6 Rancour 7 Stars 8 Dying
9 Choke 14 Eyes 16 Reap 18 Hewn out 20 Venison 21 Stash
23 Peter 24 Verse 26 Orpah 28 Eagle

No 70

Across
6 Easter Sunday 8 Avenger 9 Rhyme 10 Gain 12 Spirit
14 Titus 15 Lemuel 16 Asia 19 Sight 21 Naharai 22 Old
Testament

Down
1 Essenism 2 Hedge 3 Usury 4 Unwraps 5 Lady 6 Evangelist
7 Septuagint 11 Oil 12 Sum 13 Rosaries 14 Testate 17 Gnash
18 Wheat 20 Gold

No 71

Across
1 Ishmael 8 Shinto 9 Cluniac 11 Matthias 12 Small 14 Once
15 Edomites 17 Troubles 18 Into 20 Anger 21 Wingspan
23 Softest 24 Reeled 25 Chapels

Down
2 Solemn 3 Mingle 4 Elam 5 Rhythms 6 Anointing
7 Possessor 10 Candlemas 12 Southward 13 Accounted
16 Abashed 18 Instep 19 Teasel 22 Noah

No 72

Across
1 Seven 4 Glass 10 Glebe 11 Antioch 12 Egyptian 13 Alto
15 Inside 17 Voodoo 19 Ucal 20 Zedekiah 23 Lullaby
24 Asses 25 Study 26 Strew

Down
2 Enemy 3 Eventide 5 Late 6 Spoiled 7 Egregiously 8 Satan
9 Theosophist 14 Covenant 16 Scarlet 18 Beryl 21 Issue
22 Hand

No 73

Across

1 Crozier 7 Fowls 8 Evil man 9 Prayer 11 Flour 13 Also
14 Numbers 15 Siva 16 Myrrh 17 Enough 21 Strings
22 Skull 23 Hymnist

Down

2 Revelation 3 Zalmunna 4 Elam 5 Four 6 Play 9 Paten
10 Easter eggs 12 Smith 13 Assyrian 18 Oaks 19 Gulf 20 Stay

No 74

Across

1 Bani 5 Tyre 7 Despair 8 St George 10 Mole 12 Reba
14 Shadrach 16 Jeroboam 17 Ibis 18 INRI 19 Monarchs
22 Estates 23 Nuts 24 Ebal

Down

1 Boss 2 Idle 3 Espresso 4 Cake 5 Trimurti 6 Ease 9 Therein
11 Lachish 13 Amorites 15 Ammonite 18 Icon/Ikon 19 Moth
20 Rose 21 Soul

No 75

Across

1 Stamp 4 Snail 10 Herbs 11 Lucifer 12 Issachar 13 Enos
15 Thomas 17 Red Sea 19 Nets 20 Cantoris 23 Opinion
24 Eaten 25 White 26 Usurp

Down

2 Turks 3 Musician 5 Neck 6 Infants 7 Christendom 8 Allah
9 Trespassing 14 Feathers 16 Ostrich 18 Saint 21 Rotor
22 Mint

No 76

Across

1 Azariah 5 Left 7 Torso 8 Rebuke 10 Oops 11 Required
13 Isaiah 14 Weasel 17 Ethiopia 19 Fret 21 Adrian 22 Amice
23 Isle 24 Lioness

Down

1 Authorised 2 Agrippa 3 Idol 4 Hornet 5 Labourer 6 Fakir
9 Idolatress 12 Canonise 15 Service 16 Simnel 18 Hades
20 Halo

No 77

Across

1 Opus 4 Sparrow 8 Potiphar 9 Fir 11 Eagles 13 Speech
14 Spilt 15 Play 17 ASAP 18 Crumb 20 Ararat 21 Eunice
24 Ira 25 Grandson 26 Necktie 27 Nest

Down

2 Prong 3 Spices 4 Soho 5 Abrupt 6 Rafters 7 Worshipper
10 Temptation 12 Sport 13 Slime 16 Aramaic 18 Caught
19 Burden 22 Idols 23 Bake

No 78

Across

1 Study 4 Dross 10 Bullock 11 Bible 12 Dance 13 Raisins
15 Seth 17 Alien 19 Asher 22 Debt 25 Highest 27 Olive
29 Fatal 30 Ananias 31 Hymns 32 White

Down

2 Talon 3 Diocese 5 Rabbi 6 Sublime 7 Abide 8 Skirt 9 Feast
14 Ahab 16 Ends 18 Lightly 20 Stomach 21 Chaff 23 Ethan
24 Cease 26 Eglon 28 Idiot

No 79

Across

5 Spoon 8 Crucifix 9 Agree 10 Epiphany 11 Gnash 14 Dry
16 Aleppo 17 Easter 18 Get 20 First 24 Jonathan 25 Whale
26 Buddhism 27 Gypsy

Down

1 Acres 2 Cubit 3 Fight 4 Sinner 6 Paganism 7 Overstep
12 Almighty 13 Apostles 14 Dog 15 Yet 19 Exodus 21 Hands
22 Choir 23 Enemy

No 80

Across

1 Absolution 8 Hoodlum 9 Olive 10 Tutu 11 Mass 12 NCO
14 Useful 15 Enough 18 Tom 20 Path 21 Clip 23 Dalai
24 Aureola 25 Tabernacle

Down

1 Apostle 2 Sold 3 Lammas 4 Thousand 5 Onion
6 Whitsuntide 7 Jehoshaphat 13 Surplice 16 Unloose
17 Strain 19 Malta 22 Uric